"The be
The End of The Worl   .e Know It
is that it spells out in plain English exactly what all of us
need to know. Steve Shelley does not mince his words. He
writes with pace, authority and brevity, condensing the
exhaustive findings of experts into a few pithy sentences. We
have reached a tipping point. The planet will survive man's
reckless stewardship – but will we? There is no time to
waste. Each of us can make a difference.
This book tells you how."

Jonathan and Angela Scott: The Big Cat People

Wildlife photographers and film makers

Climate change means

The End of the World as we know it

How climate change and environmental destruction threaten our lives and what you can do about it.

by *[signature: Steve Shelley]*

Steve Shelley

I've done the research so you don't have to.

[handwritten inscription: for John of a like mind! I would love to see your own project :)]

A LonePenguin Book
www.thelonepenguin.com

Strategic Alignment Ltd, York, England

ISBN: 978-1-9162014-0-8

Foreword

Steve Shelley is an expert in getting to the heart of a subject and presenting it in an informative and digestible format. In this book, his passion for the environment and his love of writing converge. He calls himself a climate change evangelist and an advocate for the environment. But as the original founder of the UK's Bottle Bank recycling programme, he could equally be described as a social change engineer.

'The End of the World as We Know It' aims to answer the questions of what climate change is all about and what we can do about it. It demystifies the science and combines the voices of the experts with Steve's own personal observations and experience. The book faces up to some difficult challenges, recognising that the world is on a nearly unstoppable path to self destruction. It was written in the heart of the UK's Peak District National Park, a beautiful part of the country which turns out to be both an unnatural landscape and the actual 'ground zero' of the industrial revolution that set in train the problems the world is now facing. Steve's perspectives also leverage his time travelling the fast disappearing wild places of Africa.

Rarely is a book so relevant and so important. Climate change and environmental destruction may herald the end of the world as we know it, but we have a window of opportunity to consciously create a new, fairer and ultimately more meaningful society. Read this book and find out how.

Steve Shelley
Hope Valley, England

INSPIRED BY THE
PEAK DISTRICT

BE MORE LESS.

BUY LESS, BURN LESS, WASTE LESS.

BE A LESS FREQUENT FLYER.

CONTENTS

CONTENTS

Chapter 1

GROUND ZERO

Twenty miles downstream from where I write overlooking the River Derwent lies Cromford Mill, built by Richard Arkwright in 1771 to mechanise the spinning of cotton yarn. Water powered machinery transformed the way products were manufactured, and the way communities were housed around the mills transformed how people lived and worked. It took them out of home based craft and farming occupations into employed labour and shift work. Nowadays, it's a tourist attraction with tea rooms, antique shops and animated displays, a UNESCO World Heritage site.

Arkwright's system spread through the Derwent Valley and across the north of England, and by 1788 there were more than 200 such mills in the country. They set in train a whole new sort of society built around jobs, production and consumption. One of them, Bamford Mill, now converted into modern apartments, lies right in my line of sight. It's hard to imagine looking out over this placid stream that Arkwright's mill was the very first factory in what was to become known as the Industrial Revolution.

But water power technology was rapidly superseded by James Watt's newly invented 'fire engine' which brought the more productive power of steam to mines, mills and forges across Derbyshire, Staffordshire and Shropshire. A few miles away, the city of Sheffield, long famed as the Steel City, a city of cutlers, was the site of a once unique water powered grinding wheel used to sharpen the edges of knives and tools. They chipped these 'millstone grit' stones out of the nearby Derbyshire 'edges'. There was iron ore and coal too in these hills. Coal, steam and iron were a match made in industrialist heaven and the fossil fuel revolution began.

Paradoxically, I'm also right in the heart of Britain's first National Park, the Peak District. Apart from a cement works down the road in Hope, you wouldn't think of this lovely valley as Ground Zero of the Industrial Revolution. But this river that runs through it spurred almost everything about our modern technologically driven life of comfort and convenience. The mills brought us nicer clothes, softer bedsheets and prettier handkerchiefs. But unfortunately, they came at a cost: carbon dioxide emissions, pollution, population growth and climate change. Yes, this is where it all started. Millions of tons of coal extracted from the ground powered growth, technology, comfort, war and empire. Its fumes, pollution and spoil heaps were evident for all to see. In less than 250 years, we caused more damage to Planet Earth than in the the entirety of previous human history spanning hundreds of thousands of years.

Britain's noxious habits may have eased a little now, but globally they're still accelerating. Since the first warnings about 'greenhouse gases' were published in 1980, as much carbon dioxide has been pumped into the atmosphere as in the whole of prior human existence. Collectively, we've walked with our eyes wide open into the biggest catastrophe it's possible to imagine: the end of the world as we know it.

This book is my attempt to push out the message and recruit people to the cause of saving our planet. I've waded through the reports and figured my way through the science. The story I've extracted explains what is going on, how it happened, and what is likely to be the outcome. It's more that 'just' climate change. I also provide some reasoned suggestions about what we need to do to avoid the worst case scenario.

Actually it's not really about saving our planet. That will take care of itself. If it needs to shrug us off as an impediment to its stability, it will do so. What is at stake is our own species, humanity for want of a better word. The first life form to possess high levels of consciousness, with the ability to discover things beyond our immediate horizons, but also the most consumptive and wasteful, and the most destructive to our once nurturing environment. It's time to exercise our not inconsiderable imagination and technical competence to restore the balance.

We cannot trust to the natural flow of events, nor even to national and global governments. They have too much at stake in the present dispensation. It's all down to us. We've enjoyed our consumer boom, now it's time to pull in the reins, to activate the emergency brake. The threat is real. Some people are talking about extinction. Unless we act now, the world as we know it, along with ourselves and our comfortable lives, is doomed.

Arkwright's mill triggered a technological revolution. Watt's steam engine, powered by English coal, set off the industrial revolution. Together, they prompted a social revolution, in the nature of work and in the nature of consumption, in the quality of life and in the destruction of the environment. We might want to reflect on that when we come later to some proposed solutions to our present dilemma.

My activist past

Long before Extinction Rebellion, there used to be an active, not to say militant, environmental movement. Friends of the Earth. GreenPeace. Keep Britain Tidy. Keep America Beautiful. It was a bandwagon that attracted not just concerned individuals but also businesses and corporations. I was part of it. We were going to save the world.

There was a campaign against waste. Demonstrators dumped a pile of non-returnable bottles on the doorstep of the London office of Schweppes, a soft drinks manufacturer. Bottlers and their suppliers faced the threat of a consumer revolution. As a not terribly altruistic twenty something, but ready to shake up society and make a mark, I was appointed by the glass industry trade association to do something. Our response was to launch the Bottle Bank, a glass recycling scheme, designed both as a step to save natural resources and reduce waste but also to fend off possibly adverse legislation. Other arms of the packaging industry quickly followed.

In retrospect, I can claim that we set in train a generation of environmental responsibility that led to the ubiquitous carpark recycling centres and the separation at source waste disposal policy that UK councils are supposed to follow to this day. Faced with the objection that people didn't care enough to take their empties down to their local Bottle Bank, we proved them wrong. People did care.

What happened?

Forty five years later, many of those glass bottle makers are long gone, their products – returnable and recyclable – largely replaced by disposable plastics. Lighter in weight, cheaper to make and arguably more convenient, plastic packaging took the world by storm. People stopped worrying about the environment and opted instead for consumerism and instant gratification. Plastics found their way into everything. Clothes, food, packaging, cars, almost everything is made of plastics these days. And much of it finds its way into the oceans and into our food chain.

So here we are with a polluted planet, poisoned oceans and a tainted food supply. The icecaps are melting and seas levels rising. It's getting hotter. Wild species are dying off like never before. Songbirds, butterflies and bees have all but disappeared.

We might be next.

I'm sorry. I mean, it's not really my fault. I didn't ask to be born in 1950. But if I'd had the choice, I'd have to say this was a pretty good era to live in. Sure, great advances were made at other times, possibly even greater adventures were to be had. But we managed to skip the horrible wars and terrible diseases of previous generations. Exciting technological inventions of the earlier era – aviation, space travel – literally took off in our time. Comfort, convenience, freedom and adventure are what drove us. And we threw ourselves whole heartedly into a headlong hedonistic dive into living for our 'now'.

We heated our homes, we drove to work, we flew around the world on business and for pleasure. We lived life at a faster pace. We enjoyed, we consumed. TVs, phones, cars, clothes. People around the world envied and imitated us. Globalisation, we called it. Collectively, we fed and we bred like never before. We grew fat. If you couldn't afford a seat on the gravy train, the state paid for you. And then we paused to look back. In a single generation, we'd caused so much damage to our planet that it may be irreversible. In the worst case, it may become to all intents and purposes uninhabitable, unrecognisable as we know it. In the best case, to survive, our entire social structure and values will have to change.

I feel a shared blame for what is unfolding around us now. But if you asked me to give it all up for a more secure future, it would be a difficult choice. But that's now where we are. Climate change is not an opinion nor a theory, neither is it a choice. It's a visible, tangible fact. And it poses a real and present danger.

We might as well get started.

Chapter 2

THE PROBLEM

While scientists have been wringing their hands in public and schoolchildren taking to the streets in mass demonstrations, many people seem not to understand the nature and severity of the threats facing our planet. Perhaps they assume someone somewhere will sort out the mess. Perhaps they feel the problem is so enormous, it's beyond their comprehension, beyond their ability to do anything about it.

In this chapter, I'll try to explain what's happening. It can seem complicated, but the effects are all too evident for us to see. The problem came to light as a result of a measurable increase in the concentration of carbon dioxide (CO_2) in the atmosphere. For hundreds of thousands of years, the proportion of CO_2 hovered around 0.025% (or 250 parts per million, ppm). In 1950 it reached 300ppm. Now it's over 400. This doesn't sound like a lot of gas, but the problem is that CO_2, along with methane (CH_4), nitrous oxide (N_2O_2) and the CFCs that are (in China) still used as refrigerants, act as 'greenhouse' gases. They stop heat from the sun radiating back out into space and, just as a greenhouse or conservatory warms in the sunshine, so too does the earth's atmosphere.

Atmospheric carbon dioxide comes from anything that is burned: wood, coal, petrol, diesel, fuel oil, gas, paraffin, wool, cotton, plastics. All of these are 'organic' materials – they contain carbon which reacts with atmospheric oxygen to create heat, CO_2 and water vapour, and frequently several other more or less noxious gases.

By the time the first warnings were being published in the mid 80s, reports were coming in of unseasonal melting of icebergs, glaciers and ice sheets in the Arctic and Antarctic. This, it was postulated, would lead to a rise in global sea levels. As temperatures rose, weather patterns would change. Scientists developed new mathematical techniques and statistical methods to average out the widely varying temperatures around the world and come up with a meaningful number. The measure used is 'anomaly', or the difference between the current average and a reference value derived from data between 1850 and 1900. By 1960, the anomaly was 0.25°C, by 1985, 0.5°C. Now it's closer to 1°C. It was this trend, most clearly observable since the Second World War, that led scientists to suggest that the CO_2 levels and atmospheric warming represented cause and effect, and that both were the result of recent human activity.

It confused the issue that sea levels had already been rising for a long time. For hundreds of thousands of years, as ice ages came and went, the sea level rose and fell. There is plenty of evidence around the world that it is now some 30m higher than even a couple of thousand years ago, during recorded history. Human settlements have been found under many metres of sea water in diverse locations from the North Sea, to the Mediterranean, Black Sea, Caribbean and Pacific oceans. It may well have been this long term phenomenon which led some people to question the man-made 'theory' of global warming. If sea levels had been rising for millennia, why blame human activity now? This is naïve for three reasons. Firstly, those earlier rising levels had no correlation with a rising atmospheric CO_2 concentration. Some other effect was at play. Secondly, even if the current problems were not man-made, they were there anyway and would still have the same dire consequences. And thirdly, as we shall see just now, there are several other malevolent forces acting to damage the earth, all of which are solely attributable to human activity.

So, increased emissions from human activity, increasing CO_2 levels, increasing temperatures, rising sea levels. So what? We're only talking about a 1°C rise. The trouble is, the planetary climate system seems to overreact to small changes, disproportionately affecting the entire complex ecosystem of life. In the UK, June 2018 was one of the hottest on record. But the 2019 month of June was one of the coolest and wettest. That same month, parts of mainland Europe sweltered under record breaking temperatures in excess of 40°C. This instability in weather patterns is precisely what we can expect from the change in energy balance when you multiply that 1°C rise by the millions of cubic kilometres of sea water in the oceans. Ocean energy levels amplify the effect of warming, leading to greater instability and a greater incidence of extreme events such as storms, gales, hurricanes and the accompanying floods and damage. Warmer seas cause polar ice to melt faster and they kill coral reefs.

As well as increasing temperatures, CO_2 also increases the acidity of the oceans. In 2015, that 'mere' degree coupled with higher acidity killed off half of the coral forming Australia's Great Barrier Reef. That wonder of the natural world, which had existed in its magnificence for thousands of years, home to one of the world's greatest displays of marine biodiversity, was gone in a single season. Its long-term outlook was downgraded by the government in 2019 to 'very poor'.

The pace of loss of glaciers, mountain snowfall and polar ice cover has increased. Ski resorts have been obliged to close during previously busy seasons. Droughts and floods have struck widely separated parts of the world. Forest fires have killed hundreds in Greece, Portugal and California. It rained in the Arabian Desert. It snowed in tropical Kenya. And the three hottest years on record occurred within the past five years. It's plain to see that weather patterns all over the planet have departed from anything that could previously be considered normal.

We'll come later to predictions of future trends in these climatic conditions. But these are not the only problems facing Planet Earth. It's not 'just' emissions and not 'only' climate change that are damaging the environment. The world over, landscapes are being converted from their natural state into the service of humankind. This leads directly to a great loss of wild species as natural habitats are turned into towns and cities and into agricultural plantations. This not only has negative consequences for the planet and for our long term wellbeing, but it also contributes to climate change. We shall see, in fact, that many of the factors we are talking about are interlinked and have mutually interdependent causes and effects. Forests and savannas help to absorb carbon dioxide, in fact plants depend on it just as we depend on the oxygen that their photosynthesis generates. As forests have been decimated, more CO_2 is retained in the atmosphere, amplifying the trend and effects we've already observed. It may be that if we'd kept the world's big rain forests intact – in Indonesia, central Africa and South America – that CO_2 driven climate change might not be such a worry. But their destruction, aided and abetted by the overt policy of their respective governments, dramatically adds to our problems. Large tracts of these forests are in flames as I write, adding vastly to the volume of harmful emissions, directly affecting the health of nearby communities, and helping the planet on its path to doom.

Food crop plantations replacing natural forests are part of the problem, but the allocation of vast areas to livestock is even worse. Livestock – through the loss of forest, its own emissions and the industrial infrastructure around it – accounts for 15% of human caused greenhouse gas emissions.

The loss of wild spaces leads to the loss of wild species: mammals, birds, insects, amphibians, plants. At sea, pollution from effluents, acidification and plastics waste leads to a similar loss of fish, crustaceans and other marine creatures. Coupled with over-fishing, this has decimated fish stocks which have crashed in many parts of the world. As the global human population has grown, populations of wild species have declined almost exactly in line. It seems that whether for fear, for safety, for space, for food or for fun, we cannot comfortably co-exist with most other life forms. We kill them.

These trends have now gone so far that 75% of the earth's land surface and 66% of the oceans have been adversely affected by human activity. A million species face extinction. This growing imbalance is an indicator that the earth's ecosystem is sick. It has happened within our own lifetime, and it's all our own fault.

There's no doubt about this, but it may be fair to ask, so what? We have to live, we need to farm and to fish. We need homes and jobs. We are programmed to survive. But the natural world is essential for our well-being. It's a simple truth that we need nature more than nature needs us. In fact, in the worst case, Planet Earth, in its guise as Gaia, a coherent living organism, will simply shrug us off and evolve different life forms, as it has several times before. The fact is that we don't need to 'save the planet', we need to save ourselves. As Stephen Hawking famously warned, greed and stupidity are what will end the human race. But it's a dilemma: the skills and strategies that have ensured our survival now threaten it.

Diversity is essential in more ways than one. A highly varied fauna and flora is a sign of a healthy ecosystem. Some environments − for example rain forests and coral reefs − are highly diverse. Paradoxically (or perhaps not), humankind doesn't survive well in them. Others, such as the African savannas or the central Asian steppe are less diverse but may support very large numbers of particular species. Humans seem to do best in a mixed environment. Life in cities may seem to have a certain buzz about it but it lacks the greater depth and connection that life in the countryside can provide.

The opposite of diversity is monoculture. Vast acres of wheat, soy or rapeseed. Plantations of tea bushes or coffee trees. Cocoa and cotton. Huge fields of tulips. Cities full of people. Monocultures have the benefit of efficiencies. But they are prone to collapse. Disease spreads rapidly across a monoculture. Life has evolved by means of diversity. When one species suffers, another rises.

All of our foodstuffs and many of our medicines originally derived from wild plants and animals growing and thriving in wild places. While some bacteria and viruses threaten our health, we depend on others for our very existence. Our own bodies are quite literally a biodiverse environment hosting vast colonies of mutually interdependent non-human organisms.

It's easy to forget that much of the past hundred thousand years of human history has been characterised by eking a living from nature, settling in fields of plenty, and migrating when it looked greener on the other side. It proved to be a successful strategy. We survived climatic shifts, repeated ice ages and their associated calamities. It's only in the past ten thousand years that we've settled into an agrarian, and even more latterly urban, way of life. Within the past four or five thousand years, there were only a handful of significant cities worthy of the name. And, as we noted earlier, it's only for the past 250 years that we've lived in an age of industry and technology. No wonder we've messed up: it's not what we're naturally good at.

So, climate change, habitat loss, deforestation, species extinction, loss of biodiversity. This is truly terrible. But we're not done yet. Every week, every household produces bag loads of rubbish, garbage, waste, call it what you will. We expect our local councils to collect it and then it's out of sight, pretty much out of mind. We probably think some of it gets recycled but I'd bet we mostly don't really know. And I'd bet most of it isn't. It goes to 'landfill', a euphemism for dumping it all on open ground and bulldozing it into the earth. Or into the sea to help 'reclaim' some extra land.

We modern humans are a wasteful lot. It's a hallmark of our so-called consumer society. We work, we earn, we buy, we consume, we dump. That's the cycle of our lives. Take a look into your bags of waste. Probably most of it is used packaging, and most of that various forms of plastics. The use of plastics in packaging has escalated drastically in the past 30 years or so. It's lightweight, convenient and cheap. And an awful lot of it ends up in the oceans where it finds its way into our own food chain. There is a floating island in the Pacific called the Great Pacific Garbage Patch. It's mostly made up of discarded plastics. And it's the size of France. Waste, particularly plastics, has become a major export, some reportedly being dumped out of sight in Asia and Africa.

More insidious are the microscopic plastic fragments which flush out of our clothes in their billions every time we run the washing machine. Detergents and micro-plastics are poured into our drains and guess where they end up? Yup, in the oceans, into our food chain and into our bodies. Pollution of rivers and seas is helping to kill off fish stocks and make parts of the shoreline uninhabitable for marine life. But pollution of the air we breathe is killing our own people. In spite of draconian legislation and a 'congestion charge' designed to dissuade motorists from entering the capital's streets, London's air quality is one of the worst in the western world. Its pollution contravenes the standards of both the European Union and its own government. Forty thousand people are killed every year in the UK from diseases brought on by breathing polluted air, twenty times more than in road accidents. And no-one is held accountable.

Air pollution comes nowadays mostly from exhaust fumes. But even as coal is being phased out, a solution is far from in sight. Remember when cooking on gas was promoted as 'clean energy'? In the UK in the 1970s, entire towns were plumbed with pipes to transport 'clean efficient' natural gas to our homes from deposits in the North Sea. Nowadays, much of it has to be imported, from, amongst other places, Russia. Gas pipelines criss-cross Europe from East to West and LPG tankers ply the seaways. We're told proudly that power stations which used to run on coal no longer pump dust and noxious gases into the atmosphere. Some run on 'biomass', crops grown specifically to burn to produce electricity. But most generating stations run on gas turbines. Here's the shock: the result of this 'clean' combustion of natural gas is CO_2 and H_2O, carbon dioxide and water vapour, and both of these are greenhouse gases. Come on, clouds are made of water vapour, you can see for yourself that they affect the weather. They *are* the weather. It's not rocket science.

I'm going to end this chapter with some answers to a question I often hear: "Yes I've heard about climate change, but what exactly is going to happen?" The simple answer is: Look around you, listen to the news, and then multiply it by two or three orders of magnitude. Unstable and more extreme weather patterns, cataclysmic events, mass migrations, ice sheets melting, sea levels rising, new diseases, risks to life, limb and property, extinctions, health risks, financial losses and risks to the economy and jobs. Effects may be different in different parts of the world and even across different parts of the country. In the UK, and the US Midwest, it's flooding that seems the greatest immediate threat. In other countries, it's droughts, forest fires, crop failures and famines. Hurricanes are becoming more violent, with the state of Florida taking a repeated battering. Later chapters explain how these trends will play out in more detail.

You might reasonably think that any government whose policies led to these sorts of outcomes would be fast thrown out of office. It's a threat to life and limb more certain than terrorism, more likely than a nuclear holocaust. But there you go. We're living in a different world. Leadership, or its lack, is one of the burning issues.

Positive feedback loops

A feature of climate change reporting is that things seem to have got worse more quickly than anyone forecast. Here's why.

The permafrost has been melting in Siberia for thirty years already and the carcasses of long dead creatures such as woolly mammoths have been exposed. Some are almost intact. Some still have undigested vegetation in their stomachs. Many must have died and frozen within hours. They stayed frozen for 30,000 years. But permafrost is a funny thing, stretching as it does all around the arctic latitudes. It's neither ice nor earth but a squidgy mixture of both. And when it melts, what remains is a mushy slurry more akin to swamp than to dry land. It rots the roots of plants that were growing there, and – rot being a chemical reaction – this causes an efflux of methane (CH_4). Methane has an even greater greenhouse effect than does CO_2. So in turn, the planet grows warmer, which melts more permafrost, which releases more methane, which warms the atmosphere still further . . .

This is an example of a positive feedback loop. In the context of climate change, it means that the worse it gets, the worse it gets, in an increasingly vicious spiral. It's one of the reasons that forecasts of climate change impacts are tricky and that so far things seem to have got worse more quickly than predicted even a few years ago.

Methane, by the way, is not only sixty times more deadly a greenhouse gas than carbon dioxide, its concentration in the atmosphere has increased by 15% in the past 15 years, for reasons that remain unclear.

There are many other examples of positive feedback loops. As polar ice melts and decreases, the amount of solar radiation reflected back into space is reduced. Again, the effect is to speed up the warming process, which reduces solar reflection, which increases warming, which melts more ice . . .

The loss of forests reduces the absorption of CO_2 which increases warming and acidification which reduces the ability of plants to grow and causes a change in the nature of habitats, further reducing the growth of forests . . .

A complex relationship of ocean currents means that as the Amazon rain forest is reduced, local weather patterns change, reducing the flow of the Amazon river, which in turn changes the pattern of currents in the Atlantic including the Gulf Stream. In the Pacific, the well known El Niño ocean warming effect that triggers extreme weather patterns across much of the world, has now become less of a cycle than a permanent phenomenon.

As sea levels rise, the additional weight of water along coastlines can trigger earthquakes and volcanic activity. Volcanoes are one of the most dangerous sources of greenhouse gases and particulate pollution. Their eruptions can reduce the amount of sunlight, increase air temperatures, and deepen the impact of the whole cycle. Volcanic eruptions are known to have caused significant climate change at intervals throughout history.

The coal burning steam engine was invented to power pumps in order to lower water levels in deep mines. This enabled them to produce more coal from progressively deeper mines. That coal enabled the production of electricity by means of generators, it triggered the search for oil and other sources of power, and our energy gluttony accelerated.

We could go on, but I think the point is made. Positive feedback loops make forecasting difficult, and make impacts bigger, more probable, more quickly. This also serves to illustrate that reversing the warming process will take a lot more effort than setting it off in the first place. Essentially, it cannot be done. Holding global warming to any particular level will not re-freeze the ice.

Chapter 3

THE EXPERTS AND THE EVIDENCE

The science around climate change can seem complicated. Many of the published reports are technical, dense, long winded and difficult to comprehend. I've read them myself, and I've extracted a selection of what I believe to be their key findings and observations. What follows in this chapter is not opinion, it's what the experts are telling us, verbatim. It comes from a wide range of high level sources whose credibility is not in doubt.

The primary sources I've quoted from are:

FAO: the United Nations' Food and Agriculture Organisation

IPBES: the Intergovernmental Science-Policy Platform on Biodiversity and Ecosystem Services

IPCC: the United Nations' Inter-governmental Panel on Climate Change

IPPR: the Institute for Public Policy Research, a British think-tank

The Lancet: the publication of the British medical profession

NASA: The American National Aeronautic and Space Administration

NOAA: The American National Oceanographic and Atmospheric Administration

WWF: the World Wildlife Fund

IPCC CLIMATE CHANGE SYNTHESIS REPORT, 2014

This is the original report in the recent wave that hit the headlines with its dire warnings. It took six years to produce. Contributors included more than 2500 scientific experts and more than 1200 authors, from 130 countries.

"Human influence on the climate system is clear, and recent anthropogenic emissions of greenhouse gases are the highest in history. Recent climate changes have had widespread impacts on human and natural systems.

"Warming of the climate system is unequivocal, and since the 1950s, many of the observed changes are unprecedented over decades to millennia. The atmosphere and ocean have warmed, the amounts of snow and ice have diminished, and sea level has risen.

"Anthropogenic greenhouse gas emissions have increased since the pre-industrial era, driven largely by economic and population growth, and are now higher than ever. This has led to atmospheric concentrations of carbon dioxide, methane and nitrous oxide that are unprecedented in at least the last 800,000 years. Their effects, together with those of other anthropogenic drivers, have been detected throughout the climate system and are extremely likely to have been the dominant cause of the observed warming since the mid-20th century.

"In recent decades, changes in climate have caused impacts on natural and human systems on all continents and across the oceans. Impacts are due to observed climate change, irrespective of its cause, indicating the sensitivity of natural and human systems to changing climate.

"Changes in many extreme weather and climate events have been observed since about 1950. Some of these changes have been linked to human influences, including a decrease in cold temperature extremes, an increase in warm temperature extremes, an increase in extreme high sea levels and an increase in the number of heavy precipitation events in a number of regions.

"Continued emission of greenhouse gases will cause further warming and long-lasting changes in all components of the climate system, increasing the likelihood of severe, pervasive and irreversible impacts for people and ecosystems. Limiting climate change would require substantial and sustained reductions in greenhouse gas emissions which, together with adaptation, can limit climate change risks.

"Surface temperature is projected to rise over the 21st century under all assessed emission scenarios. It is very likely that heat waves will occur more often and last longer, and that extreme precipitation events will become more intense and frequent in many regions. The ocean will continue to warm and acidify, and global mean sea level to rise.

"Many aspects of climate change and associated impacts will continue for centuries, even if anthropogenic emissions of greenhouse gases are stopped. The risks of abrupt or irreversible changes increase as the magnitude of the warming increases.

"Without additional mitigation efforts beyond those in place today, and even with adaptation, warming by the end of the 21st century will lead to high to very high risk of severe, wide- spread and irreversible impacts globally (high confidence)."

GLOBAL WARMING OF 1.5°C, IPCC, 2018

This was a 'Special Report on the impacts of global warming of 1.5°C above pre-industrial levels and related global greenhouse gas emission pathways, in the context of strengthening the global response to the threat of climate change, sustainable development, and efforts to eradicate poverty'. (UN reports are known for their long windedness!) The emphasis was on persuading governments of the wisdom in trying to hold global warming to 1.5°C instead of 2°C. It has been criticised as being too conservative in the light of other forecasts in excess of this.

"Human activities are estimated to have caused approximately 1.0°C of global warming above pre-industrial levels, with a likely range of 0.8°C to 1.2°C. Global warming is likely to reach 1.5°C between 2030 and 2052 if it continues to increase at the current rate (high confidence).

"Warming from anthropogenic emissions from the pre-industrial period to the present will persist for centuries to millennia and will continue to cause further long-term changes in the climate system, such as sea level rise, with associated impacts (high confidence), but these emissions alone are unlikely to cause global warming of 1.5°C (medium confidence).

"Climate-related risks for natural and human systems are higher for global warming of 1.5°C than at present, but lower than at 2°C (high confidence). These risks depend on the magnitude and rate of warming, geographic location, levels of development and vulnerability, and on the choices and implementation of adaptation and mitigation options (high confidence).

"Climate models project robust differences in regional climate characteristics between present-day and global warming of 1.5°C, and between 1.5°C and 2°C. These differences include increases in: mean temperature in most land and ocean regions (high confidence), hot extremes in most inhabited regions (high confidence), heavy precipitation in several regions (medium confidence), and the probability of drought and precipitation deficits in some regions (medium confidence).

"By 2100, global mean sea level rise is projected to be around 0.1 metre lower with global warming of 1.5°C compared to 2°C (medium confidence). Sea level will continue to rise well beyond 2100 (high confidence), and the magnitude and rate of this rise depends on future emission pathways.

"On land, impacts on biodiversity and ecosystems, including species loss and extinction, are projected to be lower at 1.5°C of global warming compared to 2°C. Limiting global warming to 1.5°C compared to 2°C is projected to lower the impacts on terrestrial, freshwater, and coastal ecosystems and to retain more of their services to humans (high confidence).

"Limiting global warming to 1.5°C compared to 2°C is projected to reduce increases in ocean temperature as well as associated increases in ocean acidity and decreases in ocean oxygen levels (high confidence). Consequently, limiting global warming to 1.5°C is projected to reduce risks to marine biodiversity, fisheries, and ecosystems, and their functions and services to humans, as illustrated by recent changes to Arctic sea ice and warm water coral reef ecosystems (high confidence).

"Climate-related risks to health, livelihoods, food security, water supply, human security, and economic growth are projected to increase with global warming of 1.5°C and increase further with 2°C.

"Most adaptation needs will be lower for global warming of 1.5°C compared to 2°C (high confidence). There are a wide range of adaptation options that can reduce the risks of climate change (high confidence). There are limits to adaptation and adaptive capacity for some human and natural systems at global warming of 1.5°C, with associated losses (medium confidence)."

THE STATE OF THE WORLD'S BIODIVERSITY FOR FOOD AND AGRICULTURE

This report by the FAO Commission on Genetic Resources for Food and Agriculture, published in 2019, addressed the influence of global warming and land use change on agriculture and the production of food.

"BFA is affected by a variety of drivers operating at a range of levels: major global trends such as changes in climate, international markets and demography give rise to more immediate drivers such as land-use change, pollution and overuse of external inputs, overharvesting and the proliferation of invasive species. Interactions between drivers often exacerbate their effects on BFA. Demographic changes, urbanization, markets, trade and consumer preferences are reported to have a strong influence on food systems, frequently with negative consequences for BFA and the ecosystem services it provides.

"Many key components of biodiversity for food and agriculture at genetic, species and ecosystem levels are in decline. Evidence suggests that the proportion of livestock breeds at risk of extinction is increasing, and that, for some crops and in some areas, plant diversity in farmers' fields is decreasing and threats to diversity are increasing. Nearly a third of fish stocks are overfished and a third of freshwater fish species assessed are considered threatened. Countries report that many species that contribute to vital ecosystem services, including pollinators, natural enemies of pests, soil organisms and wild food species, are in decline as a consequence of the destruction and degradation of habitats, overexploitation, pollution and other threats. Key ecosystems that deliver numerous services essential to food and agriculture, including supply of freshwater, protection against hazards and provision of habitat for species such as fish and pollinators, are declining rapidly."

WWF CALL4NATURE, 6TH MAY 2019

This year, WWF took the opportunity to link its own findings with those of the IPBES, providing a useful introduction to the highlights of the actual report which follow.

"Today IPBES – the independent global scientific body on biodiversity of more than 130 Governments – publishes its report on the current state of life on Earth. The report paints an alarming picture of species extinctions, wildlife population declines, habitat loss and depletion of ecosystem services – adding to the existing wealth of evidence that we are losing nature at a dramatic and unsustainable rate.

"The report also makes clear the cause of this destruction: us. We are cutting down our forests, overfishing our seas, polluting our rivers, degrading our soils and changing our climate. This poses an urgent threat to all life on Earth – including ourselves."

GLOBAL ASSESSMENT REPORT ON BIODIVERSITY AND ECOSYSTEM SERVICES, IPBES ADVANCE VERSION, MAY 2019

The IPBES is the intergovernmental body which assesses the state of biodiversity. It has members from 132 countries. These are the headlines from the 2019 report.

- In the past 50 years, human population has doubled, the global economy has grown 4-fold and global trade has grown tenfold, driving up consumption of energy and materials and biodiversity is declining faster than at any time in human history.

- The rate of global change in nature during the past 50 years is unprecedented in human history.

- Agriculture has increased threefold since 1970.

- Timber harvesting has increased by 45%.

- Land degradation has reduced productivity in 23% of the global area.

- 75% of the land area is significantly altered.

- 66% of the ocean area is experiencing increasing cumulative impacts.

- 85% of wetlands have been lost.

- 50% of live coral has been lost.

- 25% of species – one million – already face extinction.

- Direct drivers: changes in land and sea use, direct exploitation of animals, fish and plants, climate change, pollution, invasion of alien species.

- Observed warming of 1.0°C by 2017 relative to pre-industrial levels, rising by 0.2°C per decade.

- Incidence of extreme weather events has increased and sea level has risen by 21cm since 1900.

- Marine plastic pollution has increased tenfold since 1980, affecting more than 250 species, 86% of turtles, 44% of seabirds, 43% of marine animals.

- Threats to food supply, health, social stability have increased.

- Sustainability goals cannot be met without transformative changes across economic, social, political and technological domains, otherwise negative impacts are forecast to continue until at least 2050.

LANCET COUNTDOWN ON HEALTH AND CLIMATE CHANGE, 2018

The Lancet Countdown programme is a collaboration between academic institutions across the world to provide a global overview of the relationship between public health and climate change. The Lancet is the scientific publication of the medical profession.

"Four key messages:

1. Present day changes in heat waves, labour capacity, vector-borne disease, and food security provide early warning of the compounded and overwhelming impact on public health that are expected if temperatures continue to rise. Trends in climate change impacts, exposures, and vulnerabilities show an unacceptably high level of risk for the current and future health of populations across the world.

2. A lack of progress in reducing emissions and building adaptive capacity threatens both human lives and the viability of the national health systems they depend

on, with the potential to disrupt core public health infrastructure and overwhelm health services.

3. Despite these delays, a number of sectors have seen the beginning of a low-carbon transition, and it is clear that the nature and scale of the response to climate change will be the determining factor in shaping the health of nations for centuries to come.

4. Ensuring a widespread understanding of climate change as a central public health issue will be crucial in delivering an accelerated response, with the health profession beginning to rise to this challenge.

Taken as a whole, the indicators and data presented in the Lancet Countdown's 2018 report provide great cause for concern, with the pace of climate change outweighing the urgency of the response."

LIVING PLANET REPORT, WWF, 2018

The Living Planet Report, the WWF's flagship publication released every two years – the most recent in 2018 – is a comprehensive study of trends in global biodiversity and the health of the planet.

"We are living through the Great Acceleration – a unique event in the 4.5 billion-year history of our planet – with exploding human population and economic growth driving unprecedented planetary change through the increased demand for energy, land and water.

"The key drivers of biodiversity decline remain overexploitation and agriculture. Indeed, of all the plant, amphibian, reptile, bird and mammal species that have gone extinct since AD 1500, 75% were harmed by overexploitation or agricultural activity or both.

"Invasive species are another frequent threat, their spread relying heavily on trade- related activities such as shipping. Pollution and disturbance, for example through agricultural pollution, dams, fires and mining, are additional sources of pressure. Climate change is playing a growing role and is already beginning to have an effect at an ecosystem, species and even genetic level.

"Overexploitation and ever-expanding agriculture are driven by spiralling human consumption. Creating a more sustainable system will require major changes to production, supply and consumption activities.

"Only a quarter of land on Earth is substantively free of the impacts of human activities. By 2050 this fraction is projected to decline to just a tenth. Wetlands are the most impacted category, having lost 87% of their extent in the modern era.

"In one study carried out in 46 countries in the tropics and subtropics, large-scale commercial agriculture and local subsistence agriculture were responsible for about 40% and 33% of forest conversion between 2000 and 2010. The remaining 27% of deforestation was due to urban growth, infrastructure expansion and mining.

"The Global Living Planet index, calculated using available data for all species and regions, shows an overall decline of 60% in the population sizes of vertebrates between 1970 and 2014 – in other words, an average drop of well over half in less than 50 years.

"Species population declines are especially pronounced in the tropics, with the Neotropical realm, covering South and Central America, and the Caribbean, suffering the most dramatic decline with an 89% loss compared to 1970. Nearctic and Palearctic populations are faring slightly better with declines of 23% and 31%. Habitat degradation and loss is consistently the most reported threat in all realms.

"Despite numerous international scientific studies and policy agreements confirming that the conservation and sustainable use of biological diversity is a global priority, worldwide trends in biodiversity continue to decline. Without a dramatic move beyond 'business as usual' the current severe decline of the natural systems that support modern societies will continue – with serious consequences for nature and people."

IPPR: THIS IS A CRISIS, FEBRUARY 2019

The IPPR's recent report provides a useful summary of the main findings of research in the field.

"Negative human impacts on the environment go 'beyond' climate change to encompass most other natural systems, driving a complex, dynamic process of environmental destabilisation that has reached critical levels.

"Since 1950, changes in many extreme weather and climate events have been observed, including a likely increase in the frequency of heat waves over large parts of Europe, Asia and Australia, and the frequency or intensity of heavy precipitation events in North America and Europe.

"Extinction rates have increased to between 100–1,000 times the 'background rate' of extinction.

"Topsoil is now being lost 10 to 40 times faster than it is being replenished by natural processes, and, since the mid-20th century, 30 per cent of the world's arable land has become unproductive due to erosion; 95 per cent of the Earth's land areas could become degraded by 2050.

"The average population sizes of the most threatened species in the UK have decreased by two-thirds since 1970.

"The UK is described as one of the 'most nature-depleted countries in the world'.

"2.2 million tonnes of UK topsoil is eroded annually, and over 17 per cent of arable land shows signs of erosion.

"Nearly 85 per cent of fertile peat topsoil in East Anglia has been lost since 1850, with the remainder at risk of being lost over the next 30 years."

The evidence

Climate change in fourteen self explanatory charts.

1   Global CO_2, proxy measurements from ice cores, *source NOAA*

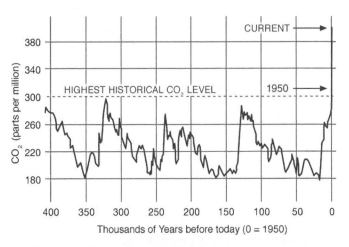

2   Historic CO_2 levels, *source IPCC*

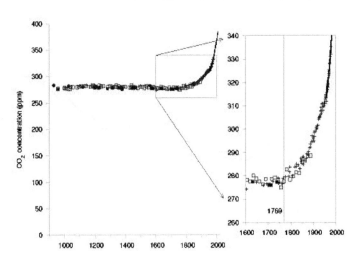

3 CO$_2$ levels, direct measurements 2005-present,
source NOAA

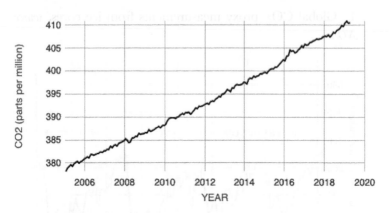

Source: climate.nasa.gov

4 Global land-ocean temperature index,
source Goddard Institute for Space Studies

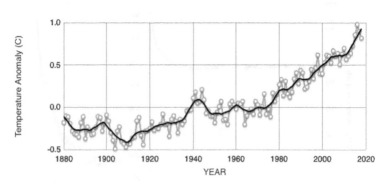

Source: climate.nasa.gov

5 Arctic sea ice, average September extent, satellite, source
NASA

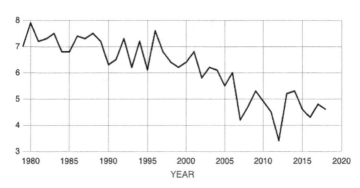

Source: climate.nasa.gov

6 Antarctic mass variation from 2002, satellite

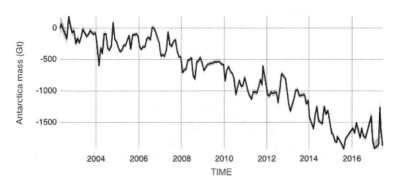

Source: climate.nasa.gov

7 Greenland mass variation from 2002, satellite

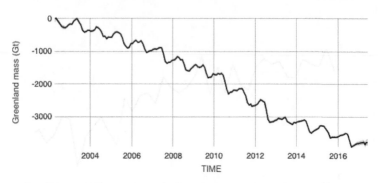

Source: climate.nasa.gov

8 Greenland surface melt area, 2019,
source National Snow and Ice Data Centre

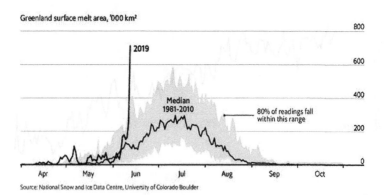

Greenland surface melt area, '000 km²

Source: National Snow and Ice Data Centre, University of Colorado Boulder

9 Sea level height variation, satellite, 1993-present

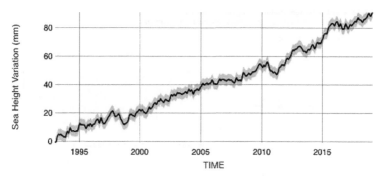

Source: climate.nasa.gov

10 Sea level change, coastal tide gauge records,
1880-present, *source CSIRO*

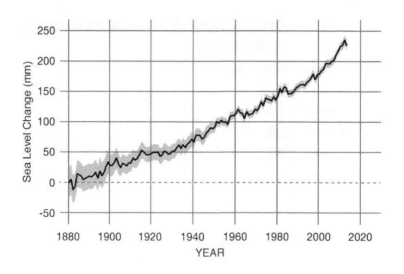

11 IPCC global warming scenarios, *source IPCC*

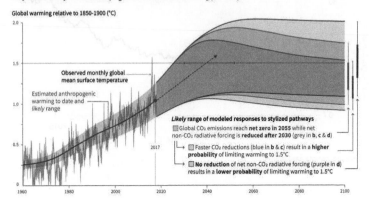

12 2018 deforestation rates

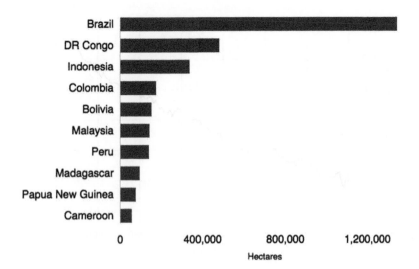

13 Peak oil production

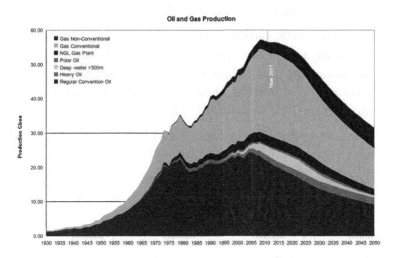

14 World population

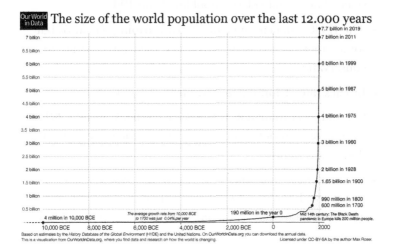

What the data tells us

In case you're the kind of person whose eyes skip over figures and charts, here's what they tell us.

- The atmospheric carbon dioxide level is 50% higher now that at any time over the past 400,000 years. It started to rise around the time of human urbanisation some 10,000 years ago but showed an abrupt steep acceleration at the precise start of the fossil fuelled industrial revolution.

- The average global temperature has risen by a full degree since 1950.

- Arctic sea ice has reduced by 40% over the past 40 years and its rate of melting has accelerated since the late 1990s.

- Arctic and Antarctic ice mass is reducing, with Greenland showing especially rapid warming, including a major melt spike in 2019.

- The average sea level has risen by nearly 2mm per year since 1880, its rate of rise doubling from 1992.

- The IPCC offers a range of global warming scenarios but some other scientists have suggested their forecasts are too conservative.

- Brazil's rate of forest loss is by far the largest.

- Oil and gas production was forecast to peak around 2015 as reserves ran out. But there is little evidence yet of any downward trend.

- The world's population is growing exponentially in parallel with the growth in fossil fuel usage, although some authorities forecast a levelling off at some point in the future.

Chapter 4

SOME VOICES

This is an arena where small voices make loud noises. Those that follow speak volumes, and they are getting louder. I'm pleased to be able to add mine. Please also add yours.

"We the undersigned, senior members of the world's scientific community, hereby warn all humanity of what lies ahead. A great change in our stewardship of the earth and the life on it is required, if vast human misery is to be avoided and our global home on this planet is not to be irretrievably mutilated."

Union of Concerned Scientists, World Scientists' Warning to Humanity, 1992

"If humans pursue a business-as-usual course for the first half of this century, I believe the collapse of civilisation due to climate change is inevitable.

"We have known for some decades that the climate change we are creating for the twenty-first century was of a similar magnitude to that seen at the end of the last ice age, but that it was occurring thirty times faster. We have known that the Gulf Stream shut down on at least three occasions at the end of the last ice age, that sea levels rose by at least 100 metres, that the Earth's biosphere was profoundly reorganised, and we have known that agriculture was impossible before the Long Summer of 10,000 years ago. And so there has been little reason for our blindness."

Tim Flannery, The Weather Makers, 2005

"Without our realising it we have poisoned the earth by our emissions of greenhouse gases and weakened it by taking for farmland and housing the land that was the home of ecosystems that sustained the environment. We have driven the Earth to a crisis state from which it may never, on a human scale, return to the lush and comfortable world we love and in which we grew up."

James Lovelock, The Revenge of Gaia: Earth's Climate in Crisis and the Fate of Humanity, 2006

"Human influence on the climate system is clear and growing, with impacts observed across all continents and oceans. The IPCC is now 95 percent certain that humans are the main cause of current global warming. In addition, the [IPPC report] finds that the more human activities disrupt the climate, the greater the risks of severe, pervasive and irreversible impacts for people and ecosystems, and long-lasting changes in all components of the climate system."

Michel Jarroud, Secretary-General, World Meteorological Organization, and Achim Steiner, Executive Director, UN Environment Programme, Climate Change 2014 Synthesis Report

" . . . there will be a near-term collapse in society with serious ramifications for the lives of readers. The paper reviews some of the reasons why collapse-denial may exist, in particular, in the professions of sustainability research and practice . . .

"Since records began in 1850, seventeen of the eighteen hottest years have occurred since 2000. Important steps on climate mitigation and adaptation have been taken over the past decade. However, these steps could now be regarded as equivalent to walking up a landslide. If the landslide had not already begun, then quicker and bigger steps would get us to the top of where we want to be. Sadly, the latest climate data, emissions data and data on the spread of carbon-intensive lifestyles show that the landslide has already begun.

"Disruptive impacts from climate change are now inevitable. Geoengineering is likely to be ineffective or counter-productive. Therefore, the mainstream climate policy community now recognises the need to work much more on adaptation to the effects of climate change. That must now rapidly permeate the broader field of people engaged in sustainable development as practitioners, researchers and educators. In assessing how our approaches could evolve, we need to appreciate what kind of adaptation is possible. Recent research suggests that human societies will experience disruptions to their basic functioning within less than ten years due to climate stress. Such disruptions include increased levels of malnutrition, starvation, disease, civil conflict and war – and will not avoid affluent nations."

Professor Jem Bendell, Deep Adaptation: A Map for Navigating Climate Tragedy , IFLAS, July 2018

"We have known for many, many years that we are driving the planet to the very brink. This is not a doom and gloom story; it is reality. The astonishing decline in wildlife populations shown by the latest Living Planet Index – a 60% fall in just over 40 years – is a grim reminder and perhaps the ultimate indicator of the pressure we exert on the planet.

"We have two main problems. First, and perhaps the greatest, is the cultural challenge. For too long we have taken nature for granted, and this needs to stop. The second is economic. We can no longer ignore the impact of current unsustainable production models and wasteful lifestyles."

Marco Lambertini, Director-General, WWF International 2018

" . . . the following three statements are now indisputable:

1 The science is solid – the Sixth Extinction is real and is happening now.

We are clearly beginning to see the effects of climate change, biodiversity loss and many other environmental and economic catastrophes, harbingers of the end of our modern world and the loss of much or most of life on Earth.

2 The proximal causes are human overpopulation and overconsumption.

Unless we can deal with the hard problem (the causes that are driving the Sixth Extinction) with a prompt and effective strategy, our feeble efforts to remedy ancillary difficulties will be of as little value as swabbing the decks as the Titanic goes down.

3 Nature does not care how difficult our human problems are.

Nature mercilessly and inexorably obeys its own natural laws of physics, chemistry, and biology, and is oblivious to our political and economic problems. To refuse to take the necessary swift and effective action because it is 'too hard' is simply giving up."

Bruce Mason, Front Row Centre at The End of the World Show, December 2018

Speaking at opening ceremony of the summit on climate change, Sir David warned the world is facing "our greatest threat in thousands of years: climate change". He urged action against the 'man-made' disaster: "If we don't take action, the collapse of our civilisations and the extinction of much of the natural world is on the horizon."

Sir David Attenborough, December 2018

"The 1997 Kyoto protocol flagged a catastrophe at 2°C, we've already hit 1°C . . . at 2°C, ice sheets collapse, 400m people suffer water scarcity, major equatorial cities become unlivable, heat waves kill thousands . . . in the worst case, by 2100, large parts of Africa, Australia, the USA, South America and South Asia could become uninhabitable – desert territories run by warlords like Somalia, Iraq and Saudi Arabia."

David Wallace-Wells, The Uninhabitable Earth, Penguin Books London, 2019

"Britain's national parks risk losing their United Nations status as globally protected nature reserves because humans are wiping out their wildlife so fast, the chairman of the Royal Society for the Protection of Birds has warned. Kevin Cox suggests that even calling them 'national parks' is misleading because farming — plus grouse shooting and tourism — is doing so much damage."

Jonathan Leake, The Sunday Times, 24 March 2019

"It is deeply concerning that in so many production systems in so many countries biodiversity for food and agriculture and the ecosystem services it provides are reported to be in decline. The foundations of our food systems are being undermined, often, at least in part, because of the impact of management practices and land-use changes associated with food and agriculture. It is also abundantly clear that the state of knowledge of many components of biodiversity, including in particular invertebrates and micro-organisms, is very inadequate and that this contributes to their neglect."

José Graziano da Silva, FAO Director-General, Commission on Genetic Resources for Food and Agriculture Assessments 2019

"On current trends, global temperatures could rise between 2°C and 4°C by 2100 and £1bn a year would need to be spent on flood management. Some communities may even need to move because of the risk of floods."

Emma Howard Boyd, Chair of the UK's Environment Agency: May 2019

"The political will to fight climate change seems to be fading at the same time as things are getting worse. We are not on track to achieve the objectives defined in the Paris Agreement. And the paradox is that as things are getting worse on the ground, political will seems to be fading."

Antonio Guterres, UN Secretary-General, May 2019

"Climate scientists may err on the side of least drama, whose causes may include adherence to the scientific norms of restraint, objectivity and skepticism, and may under-predict or down-play future climate changes. In 2007, security analysts warned that, in the two previous decades, scientific predictions in the climate-change arena had consistently under-estimated the severity of what actually transpired.

"An example is the recent IPCC 1.5°C report, which projected that warming would continue at the current rate of ~0.2°C per decade and reach the 1.5°C mark around 2040. However the 1.5°C boundary is likely to be passed in half that time, around 2030, and the 2°C boundary around 2045, due to accelerating anthropogenic emissions, decreased aerosol loading and changing ocean circulation conditions."

David Spratt and Ian Dunlop, Existential climate-related security risk, May 2019

Research conducted by an international team of scientists who examined 40 years of data concluded that the Kenyan side of the great Serengeti-Mara ecosystem has witnessed as 75% reduction in the population of larger wildlife species. One of the most protected conservation areas on earth has seen a 400% increase in human population over the past decade, putting its future in peril.

"Across the world, migratory animals – which rely on movements to find food, water and calving grounds – are under threat.

"We found extreme declines in the numbers of migrating wildebeest and loss of most migration routes in Kenya and Tanzania. Four of the five contemporary migrations are severely threatened and have virtually collapsed. This is because they are obstructed from accessing critical resources."

Joseph Ogutu, Reported in The Standard newspaper, Kenya, May 2019

"The rapid acceleration in fencing from 2014 is presently threatening to lead to the collapse of the unique ecosystem of the Great Mara within a few years. The impending cultural consequences of this loss of area may be that pastoralism and a semi-nomadic lifestyle can no longer be sustained. Ecological consequences already involve the decline of wildlife populations and may also result in the collapse of migrating megafauna populations, with secondary consequences for the rest of the ecosystem."

Løvschal et al, Fencing bodes a rapid collapse of the unique Great Mara ecosystem, www.nature.com/scientificreports, January 2017

Next is the full text of the speech given to MPs at the Houses of Parliament in London on 23rd April 2019. I had planned to edit it down and just include some pithy quotes, but this young lady is remarkable and it's worth hearing, or reading, what she has to say. Thanks to The Guardian for the transcript.

"My name is Greta Thunberg. I am 16 years old. I come from Sweden. And I speak on behalf of future generations.

I know many of you don't want to listen to us − you say we are just children. But we're only repeating the message of the united climate science.

Many of you appear concerned that we are wasting valuable lesson time, but I assure you we will go back to school the moment you start listening to science and give us a future. Is that really too much to ask?

In the year 2030 I will be 26 years old. My little sister Beata will be 23. Just like many of your own children or grandchildren. That is a great age, we have been told. When you have all of your life ahead of you. But I am not so sure it will be that great for us.

I was fortunate to be born in a time and place where everyone told us to dream big; I could become whatever I wanted to. I could live wherever I wanted to. People like me had everything we needed and more. Things our grandparents could not even dream of. We had everything we could ever wish for and yet now we may have nothing.

Now we probably don't even have a future any more.

Because that future was sold so that a small number of people could make unimaginable amounts of money. It was stolen from us every time you said that the sky was the limit, and that you only live once.

You lied to us. You gave us false hope. You told us that the future was something to look forward to. And the saddest thing is that most children are not even aware of the fate that awaits us. We will not understand it until it's too late. And yet we are the lucky ones. Those who will be affected the hardest are already suffering the consequences. But their voices are not heard.

Is my microphone on? Can you hear me?

Around the year 2030, 10 years 252 days and 10 hours away from now, we will be in a position where we set off an irreversible chain reaction beyond human control, that will most likely lead to the end of our civilisation as we know it. That is unless in that time, permanent and unprecedented changes in all aspects of society have taken place, including a reduction of CO_2 emissions by at least 50%.

And please note that these calculations are depending on inventions that have not yet been invented at scale, inventions that are supposed to clear the atmosphere of astronomical amounts of carbon dioxide.

Furthermore, these calculations do not include unforeseen tipping points and feedback loops like the extremely powerful methane gas escaping from rapidly thawing arctic permafrost.

Nor do these scientific calculations include already locked-in warming hidden by toxic air pollution. Nor the aspect of equity – or climate justice – clearly stated throughout the Paris agreement, which is absolutely necessary to make it work on a global scale.

We must also bear in mind that these are just calculations. Estimations. That means that these "points of no return" may occur a bit sooner or later than 2030. No one can know for sure. We can, however, be certain that they will occur approximately in these timeframes, because these calculations are not opinions or wild guesses.

These projections are backed up by scientific facts, concluded by all nations through the IPCC. Nearly every single major national scientific body around the world unreservedly supports the work and findings of the IPCC.

Did you hear what I just said? Is my English OK? Is the microphone on? Because I'm beginning to wonder.

During the last six months I have travelled around Europe for hundreds of hours in trains, electric cars and buses, repeating these life-changing words over and over again. But no one seems to be talking about it, and nothing has changed. In fact, the emissions are still rising.

When I have been travelling around to speak in different countries, I am always offered help to write about the specific climate policies in specific countries. But that is not really necessary. Because the basic problem is the same everywhere. And the basic problem is that basically nothing is being done to halt – or even slow – climate and ecological breakdown, despite all the beautiful words and promises.

The UK is, however, very special. Not only for its mind-blowing historical carbon debt, but also for its current, very creative, carbon accounting.

Since 1990 the UK has achieved a 37% reduction of its territorial CO_2 emissions, according to the Global Carbon Project. And that does sound very impressive. But these numbers do not include emissions from aviation, shipping and those associated with imports and exports. If these numbers are included the reduction is around 10% since 1990 – or an an average of 0.4% a year, according to Tyndall Manchester.

And the main reason for this reduction is not a consequence of climate policies, but rather a 2001 EU directive on air quality that essentially forced the UK to close down its very old and extremely dirty coal power plants and replace them with less dirty gas power stations. And switching from one disastrous energy source to a slightly less disastrous one will of course result in a lowering of emissions.

But perhaps the most dangerous misconception about the climate crisis is that we have to "lower" our emissions. Because that is far from enough. Our emissions have to stop if we are to stay below 1.5-2°C of warming. The "lowering of emissions" is of course necessary but it is only the beginning of a fast process that must lead to a stop within a couple of decades, or less. And by "stop" I mean net zero – and then quickly on to negative figures. That rules out most of today's politics.

The fact that we are speaking of "lowering" instead of "stopping" emissions is perhaps the greatest force behind the continuing business as usual. The UK's active current support of new exploitation of fossil fuels – for example, the UK shale gas fracking industry, the expansion of its North Sea oil and gas fields, the expansion of airports as well as the planning permission for a brand new coal mine – is beyond absurd.

This ongoing irresponsible behaviour will no doubt be remembered in history as one of the greatest failures of humankind.

People always tell me and the other millions of school strikers that we should be proud of ourselves for what we have accomplished. But the only thing that we need to look at is the emission curve. And I'm sorry, but it's still rising. That curve is the only thing we should look at.

Every time we make a decision we should ask ourselves; how will this decision affect that curve? We should no longer measure our wealth and success in the graph that shows economic growth, but in the curve that shows the emissions of greenhouse gases. We should no longer only ask: "Have we got enough money to go through with this?" but also: "Have we got enough of the carbon budget to spare to go through with this?" That should and must become the centre of our new currency.

Many people say that we don't have any solutions to the climate crisis. And they are right. Because how could we? How do you "solve" the greatest crisis that humanity has ever faced? How do you "solve" a war? How do you "solve" going to the moon for the first time? How do you "solve" inventing new inventions?

The climate crisis is both the easiest and the hardest issue we have ever faced. The easiest because we know what we must do. We must stop the emissions of greenhouse gases.

The hardest because our current economics are still totally dependent on burning fossil fuels, and thereby destroying ecosystems in order to create everlasting economic growth.

"So, exactly how do we solve that?" you ask us – the schoolchildren striking for the climate.

And we say: "No one knows for sure. But we have to stop burning fossil fuels and restore nature and many other things that we may not have quite figured out yet."

Then you say: "That's not an answer!"

So we say: "We have to start treating the crisis like a crisis – and act even if we don't have all the solutions."

"That's still not an answer," you say.

Then we start talking about circular economy and rewilding nature and the need for a just transition. Then you don't understand what we are talking about.

We say that all those solutions needed are not known to anyone and therefore we must unite behind the science and find them together along the way. But you do not listen to that. Because those answers are for solving a crisis that most of you don't even fully understand. Or don't want to understand.

You don't listen to the science because you are only interested in solutions that will enable you to carry on like before. Like now. And those answers don't exist any more. Because you did not act in time.

Avoiding climate breakdown will require cathedral thinking. We must lay the foundation while we may not know exactly how to build the ceiling.

Sometimes we just simply have to find a way. The moment we decide to fulfil something, we can do anything. And I'm sure that the moment we start behaving as if we were in an emergency, we can avoid climate and ecological catastrophe. Humans are very adaptable: we can still fix this. But the opportunity to do so will not last for long. We must start today. We have no more excuses.

We children are not sacrificing our education and our childhood for you to tell us what you consider is politically possible in the society that you have created. We have not taken to the streets for you to take selfies with us, and tell us that you really admire what we do.

We children are doing this to wake the adults up. We children are doing this for you to put your differences aside and start acting as you would in a crisis. We children are doing this because we want our hopes and dreams back.

I hope my microphone was on. I hope you could all hear me."

Greta Thunberg

Chapter 5

APOCALYPSE NOW

People have been predicting the apocalypse at the 'end of days' for thousands of years. They've even given precise dates for it. And sometimes waited patiently – if in vain – for transportation to heaven to escape its ravages. The only thing these forecasters have in common is that they were all wrong. There have been many times in history when things looked and felt decidedly apocalyptic. The legendary four horsemen of the apocalypse represented conquest, war, famine and plague. This fit pretty well the circumstances of the Roman destruction of Jerusalem in the year 70 when 'The Book of Revelations' was written. But its litany of disaster, destruction and death applies to many of other moments in history too.

Here are some news items from just twelve months in 2018 and 2019 that suggest we're living in apocalyptic times.

- Eight London schools were closed because of infestations by poisonous spiders.

- Polar bears invaded a town in northern Russia.

- Two 'worst ever' hurricanes struck the USA, causing the evacuation of parts of Florida. Two cyclones hit Mozambique within a month of each other, while another struck the east coast of India.

- Forest fires killed hundreds of people in Greece, Portugal and California.

- The UK enjoyed its hottest summer day on record, with roads 'melting like chocolate' and railways buckling in the heat.

- Floods in Wales were reported as the worst in 30 years.

- Ten people drowned in floods in France.

- 35 people were killed in flash floods in Saudi Arabia.

- The Ladybower Dam, which supplies water to much of the UK'S East Midlands, fell to its lowest level in decades, exposing the ruins of the flooded village of Derwent.

- The city of Cape Town nearly ran out of water, the April rains coming in the nick of time to replenish the dams.

- The UN's IPCC reported that climate change was potentially out of control and forecast a worst case scenario where a 1.5 degree temperature increase would wreak disaster around the world by 2030 (forecasts have become more pessimistic since then, in just a few months).

- Twenty of the past 22 years were the warmest since records began in 1850, and the last four years – 2015/16/17/18 – were the warmest ever recorded.

- A March 2019 report suggested Britain's national parks could lose their status as a result of their loss of wildlife and that the UK had become 'the most wildlife depleted' country on earth.

- Insect populations were revealed to have fallen to one sixtieth of what they were, along with insectivorous birds and mammals.

- Populations of predators such as foxes, badgers, red kites and spiders were on the rise.

- The UK government debated a ban on single use plastics following the revelation that vast islands of plastic waste had been found in the oceans, and that barely a few percentage points of waste plastic was being recycled.

- A dead sperm whale washed ashore in Indonesia was found to have nearly 6kg (13 lbs) of plastic waste in its stomach.

- A WWF report stated that the earth's wildlife species have been reduced by 60% since the 1970s, attributed to consumerism, overuse of resources and destruction of natural habitats for food production.

- The fashion industry was revealed as one of the world's leading polluters and sources of waste.

- Palm oil production for the processed food industry was revealed to have caused massive deforestation in Indonesia, South America and Africa.

- Medical practitioners warned that 'trends in climate change impacts, exposures, and vulnerabilities show an unacceptably high level of risk for the current and future health of populations across the world'.

- Climate change will cause the collapse of civilisation, warned Sir David Attenborough in a stark UN warning.

- A BBC news item 'casually' reported that human existence is under threat from a catastrophic collapse of the world's ecosystems.

And then we had our hottest day on record. Ever. So far. The 25th July 2019.

These news items make for alarming reading, coming as they do from a single year in which some people continued to question the reality of global warming. Almost every week there is yet another story of extreme events, whether it's devastation from a tornado in Ohio, multiple avalanches in the Himalayas, forest fires in Brazil, or glaciers melting in Greenland. But it's not only the climate that's worrying. We live in an era of religiously inspired terror attacks. The UK is suffering an epidemic of murderous knife attacks in trains, streets and parks. Shootings in schools, homes and public places have become commonplace in America. I'm not ready to suggest that society is collapsing but these are surely signs of something unhealthy. Ten years after the global financial crisis, this is the new normal. We sleep-walked into it and no-one is going to rescue us. The apocalypse is here.

The first draft of this book went under the working title of 'The Looming Apocalypse'. But it soon became obvious that signs of an apocalypse had been building around us for some time. The second draft was called 'Apocalypse Now'. Then the research started to get rather depressing, so I placed more emphasis on looking for potential solutions as well as explaining the nature of our collective problem. But I'm sorry to say that words like disaster, catastrophe, cataclysm and apocalypse still float around this subject like wasps on a plum tree in summer. These things can act suddenly but it turns out they can creep up on you too. Which, unfortunately, makes some people wonder whether it's serious at all.

So let's ask ourselves how serious a threat is this really? I mean, for years we have endured wars, earthquakes, hurricanes, epidemics, terror attacks and genocide. Unless you were directly caught up in them, life has gone on pretty much the same, aside from a few inconveniences. In any case, the first warnings about climate change were given more than 30 years ago, and disaster hasn't struck yet. Has it?

Well, talking of terror attacks, imagine that a seaside town like Southend in Essex or Miami in Florida were to be targeted by terrorists. Can you imagine what would happen?

The authorities would put the place in lock-down in a matter of moments, airports would be closed, roads blocked, life would come to a standstill. In the case of climate induced sea level rise, the threat is actually greater because it's more certain and more widespread. Isn't a call for action equally urgent? I mean, the enemy is in clear sight: it's us. We done it, guilty as charged.

The American Secretary of State celebrated the opening of Arctic sea routes between American and Asia, as if the loss of a few of his country's coastal states in exchange for shorter transit times for shipping represented a good deal. People can move away from the coast, he was quoted as saying. The world's current cohort of leaders are part of the problem, not the solution, as was the case before and after the 2008 financial crisis. This makes it unlikely that the world will come together to act coherently and therefore that the current trend, gloomy though it seems, may represent a best case scenario.

Scenarios: best case, worst case

Scenario planning is based around a range of key variables whose probability of movement is assessed. The data and forecasts shared in this book mostly revolve around a predicted temperature rise of 1.5 to 2°C as a bad but likely scenario. Lowering this forecast would require massive, immediate, concerted, global action, of which there is currently no sign. A small number of countries acting unilaterally will not materially alter the world's current path. Based on pledges to act as of mid 2019, 2.9°C is forecast. Based on a more pragmatic view of current policies, and assuming those pledges were not fulfilled in their entirety, it is 3.3°C. And if there is no concerted global action, it looks like 4.5°C. The UK's Flood Agency is counselling that we plan for a 4°C change. I've even seen a 9°C end of century forecast.

Listen and learn: it's going to be bad.

Here is the best case scenario from the IPCC. It's based on "strong participation and support for the Paris Agreement goals of reducing CO_2 emissions by an almost unanimous international community compatible with holding global warming to 1.5°C."

It assumes a shift towards electric vehicles (more than 50% by 2025), industrial scale carbon capture and storage plants operational, bioenergy sourced from agricultural wastes, algae and kelp farms, reduced meat consumption and a drastic reduction in food wastage. None of which, by the way, is yet anywhere near sufficiently developed.

Predicted outcomes include:

- relocation of some species towards higher latitudes and elevations results in changes to local biodiversity

- management demands for new ecosystems increase

- pests and diseases increase

- frequent hot summers and heavy rainfall events become more intense in mid latitudes

- coastal communities struggle with inundation from rising sea levels and heavy rainfall, with associated migration to inland areas

- frequent deadly heatwaves affect tropical cities

- the Mediterranean area becomes drier and increased crop irrigation lowers the water table

- extensive die back of coral reefs

- crop yields remain relatively stable and the most severe losses are localised and associated with extreme weather events.

That's the best case. Now here is their worst case scenario: "In 2020, despite past pledges, the international support for the Paris Agreement starts to wane. In the years that follow, CO_2 emissions are reduced at the local and national level but efforts are limited and not always successful."

Under this scenario, the report lists the following impacts:

- more frequent heatwaves
- less snow in mountain resorts
- several catastrophic years occur while global warming starts to approach 2°C
- major heatwaves on all continents with deadly consequences in tropical regions and Asian megacities
- droughts occur in regions bordering the Mediterranean Sea, North America, the Amazon region, and southern Australia
- intense flooding occurs in high latitude and tropical regions, particularly in Asia
- major ecosystems (coral reefs, wetlands, forests) are destroyed with massive disruption to local livelihoods
- drought leads to large impacts on the Amazon rainforest
- a hurricane and its associated storm surge destroys a large part of Miami
- a multi-year drought in the Great Plains in the USA and concomitant drought in eastern Europe and Russia

decrease global crop production resulting in major increases in food prices and eroding food security

- poverty levels increase to a very large scale and the risk and incidence of starvation increase considerably as food stores dwindle in most countries

- human health suffers

- there are high levels of public unrest and political destabilisation resulting in some countries becoming dysfunctional

- in spite of major decreases in CO_2 emissions, temperatures continue to rise due to the long lifetime of CO_2 concentrations

- the world as it was in 2020 is no longer recognisable with decreasing life expectancy, reduced outdoor labour productivity, and lower quality of life in many regions

- droughts and stress on water resources renders agriculture economically unviable in some regions

- major conflicts take place

- almost all ecosystems experience irreversible impacts, species extinction rates are high in all regions, forest fires escalate and biodiversity strongly decreases.

On the basis of the current state of play, the best case scenario above is almost certain. It's pretty much what's already happening. The worst case scenario is extrapolated from this and is, unfortunately, based around the status quo of limited concerted action. As noted above, the UN Secretary-General has said that just as the situation on the ground is getting worse, global support for action seems to be waning. And it has been observed that the IPCC tends towards conservative rather than alarmist reporting.

MIGRATION

Amongst the most alarming variables to be factored into our scenario planning is mass migration and its causes and effects. More than anything else, large scale movements of people driven from their homelands have the potential to disrupt economies, food supplies, political and social stability, and to trigger conflicts. Extended droughts from 2007 to 2015 across parts of the Middle East and the Eastern Mediterranean caused food shortages and price escalations. The Arab world imports much of its grain from Russia but a heat wave in that country wrecked the 2010 harvest. The price of bread soared, triggering mass dissent, the so-called Arab Spring. Demonstrations in Tunisia and Egypt led to changes in their respective governments. An uprising against the regime in Syria drove a huge number of farmers off their land and into cities. Roughly five million were displaced internally and a further six million were forced into exile by their own government's retaliatory action, directly triggering political and social instability across many parts of Europe.

Mass migration has been evident from a growing list of so-called failed states, war torn and drought-stricken countries including Somalia, Eritrea, Sudan, Libya, Syria, Iraq, Afghanistan, Zimbabwe, Guatamala and Venezuela. These displacements of millions of people count as environmental disasters, as well as being both cause and indicator of social and economic instability.

Low end forecasts for future climate-driven migration (the 'best case') propose a figure of 200 million climate refugees. That's the 2015 Syria disaster multiplied by twenty – at best. The high end worst case scenario approaches a billion.

According to UNHCR, the number of people fleeing war, persecution and conflict already exceeds 70 million – the highest number in the UN refugee agency's almost 70 years of operations. Africa and the Middle East are amongst the worst hit but they won't be alone. Already in the USA, state governments have been encouraging citizens to evacuate towns and cities in the paths of hurricanes and tornadoes. Some people will elect not to return. Migration has long been a political as well as a social and economic issue in the 'Latinisation' of America's southern states, and the most senior levels of government consistently blame Mexico. The fact is, however, that thousands of people are fleeing drought in Guatemala, and from oppression and mis-government (underwritten by the wealth of the world's biggest oil reserves) in Venezuela.

In the UK, government agencies have warned that flood defences will never be sufficient and that some low lying towns may have to be abandoned. All over the world, the most threatened and most devastated locations will become depopulated as large numbers of people move en masse elsewhere.

SOME OTHER VARIABLES

Food supply security will suffer from rising temperatures. It will be harder to produce in hotter, drier conditions with greater CO_2 concentrations. Crops will be less nutritious, and weather effects on ports will make it harder to import and export.

Diseases associated with warm climates will become more widespread. Social cohesion may break down. Democratic systems of government prized by (mainly) western societies will be shown to have failed. The capitalist system which both funded and benefited from two centuries of fossil fuelled growth will be challenged as a viable way to continue. The motivation of businesses to make money regardless of their impacts will be called into question.

It is hard to predict how all these issues will play out and over what time scale. But none of it is new. It's already happening. The potential for disruption is great, almost certain in fact. It's the end of the world as we know it. The challenge now is to adapt.

Chapter 6

SEE FOR YOURSELF

Several times during my research, I've found myself reiterating "But this is already happening". We're not so much predicting the future as observing the present. Yet as I turn and look out of my window, it would be easy to think nothing has changed. Last week's rain has given way to warmer weather. The Brits like a warm summer. But for others, a hot summer could be a death knell. To understand the bigger picture, there is nothing better than going to see for yourself at first hand.

You don't need to be a scientist. We are all more expert than perhaps you thought. Look no further than tonight's weather forecast. Almost certainly it will include the phrase "rural areas will be a few degrees cooler". What this actually means, if only they would talk straight instead of back to front, is that towns and cities tend to be a few degrees warmer than rural areas. Why? Because of the warmth generated by homes, offices, heating, traffic, exhausts, coupled with a tendency for bricks and concrete to absorb and retain heat more strongly than do fields and forests. This is human induced climate change. We know it, we see it, we feel it. It's nothing new and it's not hard to understand.

Looking out over England's green and pleasant land, you could be forgiven for thinking that the worst effects of climate change and environmental degradation will happen elsewhere and that, on the scale of things, this is a pretty safe place to live. But consider this: virtually no part of the English countryside is natural habitat. Apart from a few isolated woodlands and granite outcrops, the landscape is all human. That pretty green chequerboard of cute little fields you can see from the air is all false, the legacy of an ancient feud between aristocratic land owners and the rest of us, from a time when 'common' land was considered 'wasteland'.

Many British national parks, celebrated as wild places, are little more than hill farms for sheep, surrounded by moorlands managed for rearing pheasants, shooting grouse and hunting deer. Britain has become one of the world's most wildlife depleted places. 'Keepers' protect their masters' 'game' by illegally trapping wild mammals and poisoning birds of prey: a satellite tagged hen harrier was found shot in North Yorkshire in early 2019. The heather which covers these peat bog moorlands is an alien introduction, replacing sphagnum moss killed off by acid rain. Over time, oak trees, deer and swans have variously been deemed to be 'owned' by the ruling aristocracy for their own purposes. The so-called 'New Forest' was planted to replace the old one which had been cut down to make ships. It's not the natural broad-leaved forest it seems to be. And ponies do not count as wildlife. So if the UK seems less at risk than some other places, it's only because we've already ruined it.

Elsewhere I've seen for myself landscapes ravaged in real time by a changing climate. At the edges of the Sahara Desert in Niger, people pull up bushes and cut down the few remaining trees for firewood. They trek for miles to fill plastic bottles with water from shrinking dirty lakes. The desert sands have been creeping south for a long time. It's a recognised process of desertification, and it's made worse by the changes going on elsewhere.

In Spain's Costa del Sol, the dry bed of the Guadalmedina River that once flowed through Malaga is testimony to the difficulty in managing natural phenomena. Violent floods used to afflict the city, so a dam was constructed upstream in the hills to help regulate the flow of water. But now the river rarely flows at all. It's an eyesore in an otherwise delightful city.

Last February, I had the chance to visit Arizona. Flying high over the Arctic parts of Canada, I could see that the sea ice which usually covers Baffin Bay at this time was thoroughly broken up, leaving large areas of ocean unfrozen. On the ground, I found remnants of winter snow, but within a week temperatures had soared into the 30s (80s in Fahrenheit). The relentless build up of heat would send the over-wintering 'snowbirds' back north leaving their homes empty for the summer. That year, Phoenix's normally busy Sky Harbor International Airport was closed, because at 50°C the air wasn't dense enough to keep aircraft aloft.

Phoenix is a pretty good example of sprawling urbanisation, of the process of replacing the natural landscape and the wild fauna and flora of the incredibly diverse Sonoran Desert with human development. The city was founded in 1870 with just 240 residents. In 1950, the population had grown to 100,000. Now the city itself is home to 1.6 million people, while the greater metropolitan area, including the now contiguous cities of Glendale, Scottsdale, Tempe, Mesa and several others, adds up to a whopping 4.2 million. From Buckeye in the west to Apache Junction in the east, it's more than seventy miles and it takes over an hour to drive across it.

This is just one example of how humanity spreads like a plague across the land. It took only 150 years. Sometimes you don't need to understand the science, just use your eyes.

A story out of Africa

Some years ago, I took time off to go travelling across Africa. 16 countries 24 months, 40 national parks and reserves, three big deserts, rain forests, savannas, mountain glaciers and marine coral reefs. It was an amazing opportunity to see at first hand what these wide open spaces looked like before too much human intervention had spoiled them, to see for myself just how numerous were the wild animals on the plains before roads and fences came to disturb them. I planned to be away for a year but I ended up spending 30 years living in Africa.

By the time climate change reports were being published and warnings issued, I didn't need to be convinced. I'd already seen it. The continent's two highest mountains, Mts Kenya and Kilimanjaro, are the remnants of huge free standing volcanoes and they dominate the skyline from miles away. Over time, the shrinking of their snow caps and glaciers was clearly visible. You could see as well roads, roundabouts and shopping centres being carved out of virgin forest. This is happening at an ever increasing rate, by conscious policy and design, to accommodate a rapidly growing population, to stimulate moribund economies, and to enrich a handful of 'investors' and politically connected entrepreneurs. It's the same all across the continent. The politicians' call-out to conservationists is: "Who is more important, people or animals?" Animals don't vote so they don't get a say. But I think it's pretty obvious that if we pander only to humans then it's bye-bye wildlife. Which is exactly what's happening.

The great rain forest of the Congo basin looks from above like a collection of giant green and bubbly broccoli heads. But from within, it's dark, silent and oppressive. It may be an ideal environment for frogs, insects and birds but for humans it's not. The few indigenous tribes who eke a living here miss some essential nutrition in their diet and their growth is stunted. We call them Pygmies. Their prowess as hunters is legendary, and they'll forage for insects and tubers. But they lack vital vitamins. Nutrients in the rain forest recycle amongst the foliage and the creatures, plants and fungi that live amongst it. But the soil is quickly leached bare when forest is cleared, and it can support hardly a single year's crop production without the application of artificial fertilisers.

The real threat to the rain forest, however, is not from the hunter-gatherers, but from corporate, commercial, big business, large scale operations to fell huge groves of statuesque mahogany trees and plant in their stead serried rows of oil palms. Once considered the ultimate answer to food processors' dreamiest wishes, palm oil finds its way into a long list of foodstuffs, as well as into shampoo and beauty products. It is typically labelled generically as 'vegetable oil'. In its processed forms, it is recognised as a threat to human health, right up alongside things like sugar and monosodium glutamate.

This is not the place for an exposé of palm oil and its use by some of the world's greatest corporations – who proudly set out their pro-environment policies in their annual reports – but rather to observe its role in contributing to the destruction of our natural forests. In any case, there are several other equally damaging plantation crops, for example rubber, cacao, bananas, pineapple. The list of animals, birds, plants, insects and other life forms threatened and brought to the verge of extinction by this loss of rain forest is long and getting longer.

I've ventured into these forests in Cameroon, Congo and Uganda. Their disappearance is a real and present threat to wildlife and to carbon absorption in Indonesia and South America, as well as in Africa. Deforestation threatens those human communities, too, who have managed to remain in relative isolation from the rest of our so-called development, until loggers and planters turned up to uproot their traditional way of life.

Rain forest carpeted the shores of Lake Victoria right into present times. Much of it has now gone. It's home to malarial mosquitoes, and great blue touracos cackle from the remaining branches. Vast black clouds of lake flies undulate over the shoreline. In this part of Uganda, well meaning aid workers came with the idea for villagers to plant vanilla to enhance their income and improve their AIDS-stricken livelihoods. So many took this up that the market price of the sweet spice tumbled. You can find cheap vanilla pods in supermarkets and delicatessens all over nowadays. The forest disappeared and so too did the promised wealth of the villagers. Rain forest takes a long time to revert to type once it's been cut and planted. Meanwhile it looks like some apocalyptic jungle that's been blasted by nuclear fallout.

Lake Victoria acts as a vast weather machine for Central Africa, pumping out enormous cumulus clouds that pile into the air like giant castles. Later in the day they grow dark and menacing, transmogrifying into indigo cumulo-nimbus that arc with lightening and reverberate with thunder. They sail through the skies from lake to land where they dump their loads of water in pillars of rain onto what's left of the forests. But the pattern has been shifting. The lake is becoming covered with an alien plant, water hyacinth.

Originally introduced as a decorative flowering pond plant, it now smothers hundreds of squares kilometres of Lake Victoria, depriving the water of essential oxygen and slowing the transpiration of water into the clouds. Fishing for tilapia used to be big business here, as well as a vital subsistence source of protein. But now it's only the giant Nile Perch that roam the depths. They grow so big, they damage the villagers' nets and lines. Alien introductions like these are another main cause of biodiversity loss and environmental degradation.

Tea is another alien introduction. Tea bushes grow well in this high altitude rain forest environment. Vast estates have been carved out of the forest in Uganda and in western Kenya. They stretch to the horizon in a verdant baize. As tea became one of Kenya's staple export crops, more and more forest has been cut down, by all kinds of people for all kinds of reasons. It's as if everyone said to themselves, well if big corporations under government approval can do it, so can we. The nearby Mau Hills was, until recently, one of Kenya's last patches of indigenous rain forest. It acted as a 'water tower', feeding the Mara River which flows into the famous Masai Mara game reserve and forms its primary artery, supporting, until recently, vast herds of wildlife. But ever longer dry seasons are affecting the tea. The Mau forest has all but disappeared. And the Mara River has slowed to a pathetic trickle. The wildlife numbers, formerly one of the world's greatest spectacles, have dropped by 75%. Nowadays, the wildebeest migration, once estimated to number two million animals, can also slow to a trickle. In season, there may be more tourist vans lined up along the river than there are wild animals.

For generations, the Masai people whose ancestral territory spans the savanna plains astride the Kenya-Tanzania border lived in harmony with the wildlife around them. Their 'day jobs' revolved around cattle herding, safeguarding their assets-on-the-hoof. Frequently, especially at night, they warded off the predations of lions, leopards and hyenas. When you live amongst such creatures, it's tempting to think there should be fewer of them. But there was a balance. Even now, many of East Africa's greatest parks and reserves lie in Masailand. But never mind the predators, peaceable species like giraffes and zebra have all but disappeared in parts of the territory too. So what happened? This is not a matter of the growth of highways and cities, nor even of casual poaching. It's a matter of land ownership, and a battle between the state, indigenous land owners and the ubiquitous modern profit motive.

I have personal experience of working with Masai communities, with conservation agencies, and with the parks authorities of Kenya and Tanzania. Here are a couple of things I've seen happen. Let's start with poaching. It's always been the case with people who live on the land that some like to catch meat for the pot. It's part of our long-established hunter-gatherer programming. When it's at a low level, it's referred to as 'subsistence hunting'. But in East Africa, this has escalated into a full blown commercial butchery trade. Zebra meat has been sold in village shops as beef. At one point, ostrich farming became so trendy that wild ostriches virtually disappeared, corralled into farms. Giraffes, until recently a common sight close to Nairobi's international airport, have disappeared, slaughtered for meat, for their skins and for their decorative tails. Our attention was distracted by threats to elephant and rhino, but the once common – and totally harmless – Masai Giraffe has now too been declared an endangered species. We blinked, and it's gone.

Since Chinese workers were brought in to help build roads, almost every living thing – including stray dogs – has been rounded up and brought to their camp kitchens. Poaching of elephant and rhino, to supply east Asian markets for trinkets and potions, is well known. It's operated on an industrial scale. Less well known is the depletion of the pangolin, or scaly ant eater. In April 2019, some 14 tons of pangolin scales from an estimated 36,000 creatures, was intercepted in Singapore. The International Union for Conservation of Nature (IUCN) has declared pangolins as a species threatened with extinction. It is reckoned to be the most widely illegally trafficked mammal in the world, disappearing while our minds are distracted.

These are examples of conscious, industrial scale, commercial killing, conducted in spite of laws supposed to prevent it. But equally devastating, although perhaps more insidious, are the unintended consequences of policy and decision making. And none more so than when social, economic and conservation issues clash. In recent years, the Kenyan government has broken up the Masai's ancestral communal lands and allocated land titles to individual families. This presents a dilemma. Should these families use their newly allocated land for their own subsistence? Amalgamate with neighbours in a commercial farming project? Or leave things as they are for the benefit of wildlife and conservation? Families members often disagree. But there is little incentive to leave the land alone. For wildlife, it's a death knell.

One project I was involved with offered to lease such family plots as a conservancy at the edge of the great Mara-Serengeti ecosystem. One way of funding conservation is to develop tourist facilities. Our project planned to build an eco-lodge on a hundred leased acres. Across the river from the Masai, Kipsigis honey hunters threatened to burn down the riverine forest in pursuit of bee hives. We offered a modest payment to stop them doing that. But a consortium of conservation agencies placed a moratorium on further tourism development and we were unable to proceed. Some families were offered better deals to turn their land over to wheat farming. As a direct result, our Masai family planted wheat and the honey hunters destroyed the forest. The law of unintended consequences, and an illustration of the difficulty in decision making amid competing agendas.

Some Masai families have sold their land blocks. Settlements have been constructed, roads built, bigger herds of cattle acquired, smallholdings fenced off. The old ways are being abandoned. As a result, ancient migration routes have been blocked and, as we've noted elsewhere, 75% of wildlife numbers have been killed off in just the past few years. Progressively, this vast tract of ancient land on which the Masai and their wildlife had co-existed for centuries has been whittled away. In a single generation, the traditional balance has been subverted to the quest for profit.

This part of east central Africa is a mosaic of interconnected ecosystems, with plains, woodlands, lakes, wetlands, mountain ranges and fragments of rain forest. It's beautiful and highly biodiverse, and most probably it's where our own human species first evolved. Many people feel an immediate almost spiritual bond with this special part of the world. But, sadly, it's changing. And its change will change us too.

At the edge of the Kalahari nestled between the stark desert and the meandering waterways of the Okavango Delta, lies the little town of Maun. When I first visited, it was barely more than a crossroads in the desert. Whichever way you came, you had to navigate 200km of rough dirt roads, either from Francistown on the Zimbabwe border to the east, or from Namibia via Ghanzi in the west. In the town itself, you needed to engage four wheel drive just to get to the bank or across to the one small hotel. But even then, there was great controversy about The Fence.

Until they discovered diamonds and copper and coal, Botswana's most important industry was cattle. But due to the desert-like grazing conditions, vast areas needed to be allocated for ranching. In the north of the country, the value of national parks for conservation and tourism was recognised, as were wild areas allocated as commercial 'hunting blocks'. This was and still is home to one of Africa's and the world's greatest density and diversity of wildlife. So, to protect both the cattle and the wildlife, the government put up hundreds of kilometres of fencing. Well, it didn't protect the wildlife. It was there to prevent disease spreading from wild buffalo to domesticated cattle. What it did was prevent animals migrating. Between desert and seasonal rivers, migration is precisely what they needed to do. Anyway, the cattle over-grazed their reserved areas, created more desert, and the ranchers demanded more territory. It's what happens.

The road north from Maun skirts the fringes of the delta on its way towards a vast national park abutting the Chobe River. For the most part, the journey would be slow going on soft sand and we were often delayed by lions and elephants blocking the route. But now they've tarred the roads in and out of Maun. They've built an international airport. And the town itself has expanded with hotels to serve a new generation of high end tourists and suburban estates to house those running them. The relevance to our story? The more people that live here, the more visitors that come, the more the wildlife retreats, the more development takes place. On the positive feedback loop principle, waterways are drying up, the wildlife retreats further (and there's less of it), people go further to look for it, more lodges are constructed, more airstrips, more roads . . . and so it goes on. And Botswana is – on African standards – low on population and relatively high on good governance.

Deserts have been expanding and waterways shrinking in Africa for a long time. In some of the remotest heartlands of the Sahara lies proof of the millennial nature of climate change. It took us three days to trek with donkeys and camels and Berber guides from the oasis of Djanet high into the jagged Tassili massif where some of our distant human ancestors used to live and hunt. I don't know if this was any kind of paradise on Earth or a prototype garden of Eden, but to judge from the paintings on rock faces and in caves, this vast region was a diverse rangeland full of wildlife much like East Africa is now. There are pictures of lions, giraffe, elephant, antelope from around 8,000 years ago. Later came cattle, camels, horses and Roman chariots, illustrated in their turn.

A protracted process of desiccation has been going on here for millennia. The desert sands creep still further every year. It's not a new phenomenon. The sceptics may be partly justified: there are indeed natural cycles at play. It's just that the human-induced acceleration we're talking about in this book has brought it to a whole new level much more quickly. What is new is the ever increasing number of people who try to eke a living on its edges in countries like Niger, Chad, Burkina Faso, Mali, Libya and Sudan. Look at the list, there's barely a stable country in the entire region. Lands of arid desert and semi-desert, including those in the Horn of Africa, North Africa and throughout much of the Arabian peninsular and the Middle East, tend to act as a tinder box for tension and conflict. The fact is they're inhospitable. It's really hard to live there. Everyone is in competition to survive on the few resources as are available. Getting out – migrating – can seem like a good option.

In the northern hemisphere we've been lulled into a false idyll that warm weather equals summertime equals holidays equals good times. But in other parts of the world, warmer weather means drought, famine and starvation. It's intriguing to speculate that it was climate refugees fleeing the drought ridden Sahara that led to the start of the great Egyptian civilisation which endured for three thousand years until even that succumbed to the encroaching sands.

Encroaching sands, that's a nice metaphor for what we're all facing now.

Chapter 7

CREATURES OF THE CLIMATE

The ultimate reason that climate change is of such critical importance to us is that we are quite literally creatures of the climate. Our bodies, our communities, our cultures and our civilisations have all been moulded by the climate. Our entire existence as a species has evolved in response to the shifting climate. A changing climate facilitated our great migration out of Africa hundreds of thousands of years ago. The resilience gained from surviving repeated ice ages enabled us to colonise every corner of the planet. Sun and rain, light and dark, heat and cold, flowering, fruiting and decaying, these are the forces that shaped us. Without doubt or exaggeration, as a species and as communities, we are creatures of the climate. And that means as it changes again, we too shall change. In this chapter, I shall try to explain exactly what happened.

Modern humans, the species *Homo Sapiens* of which we are all members, emerged with all of our features, characteristics and abilities – but none of our knick-knacks nor knowledge – in the highland lake region of East Africa about 200,000 years ago. Their first venture out of Africa took place around 125,000 years ago, following the Nile to the Mediterranean and thence eastwards along the coastline as far as modern Syria. The journey was made possible by an ice age which cooled the region, lowered sea levels and opened the desert barrier across Sinai and Gaza. But it proved to be a dead end. A hot dry period followed, re-establishing desert conditions which barred their way further and closed off the the route back home. This group died out, isolated from other humans.

Tens of thousands of years passed. Through repeated cycles of climatic change, the varied geography of East Africa nurtured these early humans. The region roughly encompassing modern Uganda, the southern parts of Sudan and Ethiopia, Kenya and northern Tanzania, is a mosaic of climates, ecologies and species. Whatever the weather elsewhere, ice driven drought or flooded heatwave, this part of the world creates its own weather. Its location astride the equator ensures that whatever happens at the poles has minimal effect here. Its altitude of four to six thousand feet above sea level isolates it from incoming tides and tsunamis while ensuring there is amenable temperate weather somewhere all the time. When the world grows warm, you can retreat higher into the hills. When an ice age threatens, you can move into the lowlands. The Great Lakes provided unceasing fresh water throughout all these cycles. Animals for hunting and foodstuffs for foraging were plentiful. For a very long time there was little incentive to move elsewhere.

The probability is that these earliest ancestors of ours would have been similar to the surviving bushmen such as the San and !Kung tribes whose few remaining members are now confined to the harsh drylands of the Kalahari and Namib deserts in south west Africa. These people are amongst the world's last hunter-gatherers. For nomadic people, living literally hand to mouth, when the weather changes, you have to move on. One day without water, one night exposed to freezing rain, one week without food, and your family group dies out. Foraging, scavenging, and moving on, these are the things that keep you alive.

At the peak of another ice age, a small group of people found themselves on the shore of the far north eastern edge of Africa, perhaps what we now call Djibouti or Eritrea. But at that time it wasn't a shore and it wasn't on the edge of a harsh desert as it is now. It was just another stretch of land made habitable by lower global temperatures and lower sea levels. The Red Sea was a big salty lake, cut off from the main Indian Ocean. Without even knowing what they had done, this group set up camp in what we now call Yemen. Corroborating DNA evidence with climatic data, we know this must have happened around 85,000 years ago. One of the ladies in the party, just one, is the ancestor of all modern non-Africans. Through the female lineage of mitochondrial DNA, everyone can trace their ancestry back to this one person. It's kind of nice to call her Eve.

Eve and her band probably numbered no more than a dozen people. They lived by beachcombing, gleaning foodstuffs from the shore, and camping where they could find fresh water, at springs or near river mouths. We know they ate oysters because piles of ancient shells have been found in this very area. In this way, slowly meandering along the seashore, humans spread all around the coastline of south Asia, to Pakistan, India, Burma and Indonesia. It took ten thousand years.

During the next ice age, now around 65,000 years ago, sea levels fell again, and New Guinea and most of the larger islands of modern Indonesia comprised a continental land mass attached to south east Asia. Further onward movement would have required some island hopping and people took to the seas. It was a short hop to Australia. Indigenous Australians are amongst the oldest unmixed populations on earth. They've been there all that time. But sea levels rose again, cutting them off. Neither New Guinea nor Australia received any further influx, and didn't mix with each other either. People retreated into their mountains and deserts and lived in isolation for tens of thousands of years, right into the modern era.

The next mild inter-glacial period enabled the peopling of Eastern Europe and Central Asia, so that by 50,000 years ago, humans were arriving in parts of Europe. Their routes passed through Turkey into the Balkans, and across the then dry bed of the Black Sea into Ukraine and thence towards Poland and Germany. The glaciers which blanketed Siberia, Russia and Scandinavia opened from around 45,000 years ago. People moved up the Indus Valley across the mountains into the Kazakh steppe and onwards into this vast unoccupied – and still sparsely populated – region. China was occupied from two separate directions: an eastward migration into the north along the Yellow River, and from the south following the fertile plains of the Yangtse.

By around 30,000 years ago, humans had settled Western Europe and we see evidence of their lifestyle and culture from cave paintings of the large mammals which they hunted. People spread too from central Asia north east to Siberia, the farthest point of Asia where it links to America. The bridge which took people across this last human frontier was not the result of lower sea levels but a frozen ocean which joined the Aleutian Islands in a sea of ice. The journey could only have been made by people already accustomed to living in Arctic conditions. The last time this would have been possible was around the height of the last major ice age, the so called Last Glacial Maximum (LGM) around 19,000 years ago. There may have been two or more separate migrations into the Americas. The first went south east across Canada towards the US east coast and thence into parts of central America. This was between 19,000 and 15,000 years ago. The second wave followed a route down the western seaboard of the USA and continued all the way down so that by 12,500 years ago all of central

America and the coastal regions of South America had also been occupied.

That, in a nutshell, is the story of us, the people we think of as modern humans. As a species, we have survived multiple ice age cycles, at twenty thousand year intervals, since we set off on our great migration out of Africa. From these inauspicious origins, and against enormous odds, we peopled the entire planet. We learned to live, and finally to prosper, under vastly differing climatic and geographic circumstances through our ability to improvise, to innovate, learn, adapt and move on.

Right up to the final phase, some 12,000 years ago, all humans all over the world – and there weren't many of us – still lived pretty much the same subsistence makeshift lifestyle that we started out with, hand to mouth hunting and gathering, with few possessions and fewer comforts. Migration itself was an evolutionary response to changing weather patterns and the availability of foodstuffs. We adapted to different zones, and learned to digest different foods. We lived in harmony with nature but at the same time we were forced to battle its worst excesses. Perhaps it was discovering how to make fire that encouraged us to fight back. Fire enabled us fend off the cold, extend our diet, and create a social focus. But it also set us on our protracted mission to turn wood into smoke, carbon into CO_2. You could argue that our own evolution made it inevitable that planetary damage would ensue.

But then something else changed. What made us settle down into the societies that are the recognisable forerunners of today's patterns of living, the so-called dawn of civilisation? The answer again lies with the climate, and another ice age. The world had been warming after the

LGM, but 12,800 years ago the temperature in the northern hemisphere plummeted by 15°C over a period of less than forty years. 1300 years later, there was an abrupt shift back to warmer conditions. This took less than five years. Yet another cold snap occurred around 8,200 years ago and another at 4,200. The record shows again that the climate changed rapidly, within a single human generation. The Sahara had blossomed into a vast savanna, but the cyclical shift brought back drought and desertification. People were forced to migrate towards the perennial waters of the Nile and Euphrates river systems. They congregated into the biggest communities that humankind had yet experienced. And when large numbers of people came together in one place, they were obliged to find ways to cooperate and to cultivate in order to survive under these novel conditions. It was this crowding along the banks of the Nile, the Euphrates, the Indus, the Yangtse and Yellow rivers that created the first towns. In these locations, and at this time, we find the first true cities and all that goes with them in terms of structure and culture: leadership, administration, accounting, market trading. Climate change and environmental degradation had forced people not just to move but now to change their lifestyles.

At various times throughout human history, great deluges had swept the earth as ice sheets and glaciers melted and released their pent up waters. Entire communities were sometimes annihilated by sudden and torrential floods. 12,000 years ago, vast torrents flooded across North America, destroying everything in their path. 7,000 years ago, people living in pastoral settlements in what is now the Black Sea, awoke to find water flooding around them. The rising waters had breached the straits of the Dardanelles and swept across their homeland. So terrifying were these cataclysmic events, they seared an indelible mark into our collective psyche. The memory of that ferocious destruction is echoed in flood legends from many parts of the world. But in just one location, written records survive to tell us that at least one society counts its very existence in terms of before and after a great flood.

The retelling of a Sumerian folk tale, as recounted to a group of Jews exiled in Babylon, has been preserved as part of Christian scripture. It's taught in European and American schools to this day as if it's fact. Perhaps it is. We now know that parts of the previously dry Persian Gulf, where these first civilisations opened the written record of modern human history, were repeatedly flooded around 5,000 years ago. Settlers in the earliest Mesopotamian cities of Ur and Erech were driven from their ancestral homes. In ignorance, it was attributed to the displeasure of the 'gods'. Noah and his Ark became primal avatars for survival against the worst excesses that nature – the 'gods' – can fling at us.

Our never ending battle with an apparently capricious nature led our species into a quest for explanations and influence which can be seen all over the world in stone circles, temples, churches, mosques, synagogues, astrolabes, horoscopes and UFO sightings. There is a powerful argument to suggest that the entire edifice of religion arose as a response to this collective recollection of divine displeasure. And that our attempts to appease this deification of natural forces has diverted our attention from the real causes. Lost civilisations from Peru and Mexico to Cambodia, Egypt and Iraq owe their demise not to an inability to comply with divine demand but rather to natural cycles of climate change. In our worst misguided excesses, vast numbers of our own children were slaughtered as sacrificial offerings to these gods who, it was supposed, controlled the weather. Faith in the supernatural led entire societies to the conviction that an afterlife was more important than this present one with all its uncertainties and tribulations. If damaging the planet was a necessary sacrifice then so be it. The malevolent influence of religion caused us to believe that we owed it to our gods to mould the world to our needs. "Be fruitful and multiply", says the god of the Jews and Christians. "And replenish the earth and subdue it." We followed these instructions to the letter. The earth has been thoroughly subdued. Seas are polluted, forests levelled, cities built over fields, lakes desiccated, ice caps melted. Large numbers of wild animals – "every living thing that moveth upon the earth" – slaughtered and exterminated. That god should be proud of our achievements. Except for one thing: the instruction was never given. It was imagined, in retrospective justification for what we were already doing.

We were deceived. It turns out that the health of our planet is the only thing that matters. Some of the older pagan gods and goddesses perhaps more accurately reflected our total dependence upon the forces of nature, the climate and the environment. In the northern hemisphere, our annual cycle of festivals continues to reflect this legacy of natural knowledge: mid winter's darkest day celebrated as Yuletide in late December, the spring festival of Eostre in March, May Day, the Harvest Festival at the start of autumn in late September, and the fearful onset of winter on 31st October. Perhaps it would have been more realistic to have recognised the sun as the god of all energy. Come to think of it, maybe some of them did.

It was climate change that enabled the great migration out of Africa. It was climate change that enabled the ten thousand year trek around south Asia into Australia. It was climate change that opened up central Asia, Europe and China. It was climate change that made passable the Bering land bridge into the Americas. The distinctive skin pigmentation of our so-called races evolved from our different exposure to sunlight and from geographic isolation brought on by climatic shifts. It was climate-driven environmental degradation that impelled people to converge on rivers and settle in towns. It was climate change and environmental degradation that made possible the domestication of wild animals and wild crops. And it was the continuing cycle of drought and floods which caused empires to rise and fall.

Quite literally we are creatures of the climate. Because modern humans evolved in a time of ice, we are deeply programmed to abhor the cold and protect ourselves from it. We're programmed to seek warmth. But unfortunately, we have developed no ability nor defence for living in a climate that is too hot. We can survive and thrive between 15-25 degrees, 10-30 at a stretch. It's a narrow range. Without an amenable climate and shelter from its excesses, we suffer and die. The weather – wind and heat, rain and cold – affects our health, our moods, and our activities. Nowadays, those effects are perhaps most visible in our shopping trips and holidays. The so-called Seasonal Affective Disorder (SAD) – a winter depression – acknowledges our physical and mental need for sunlight. Police forces acknowledge an increase in violent crime during heat waves. We are truly creatures of the climate.

Our own worst enemy

The past 10,000 years has been an uncharacteristically 'stable' period which enabled us to evolve into an agricultural, urban civilisation, and to breed like never before. Our history tells us that stability and sustainability are transient phenomena at best. And that stability now seems to be shifting. The climate made us what we are. It moulds us, it nurtures us, it destroys us. It will do so again. In times gone by, when opportunity or threat arose, we were able to get up and migrate into more amenable territory. But now, as human migrations continue, it is no longer into unoccupied lands. Conflict seems inevitable.

It's in our nature to destroy. We look at an empty landscape and we see opportunity: farms, plantations, housing estates, shopping malls, networks of highways, tower blocks. This is what we proudly label as development and progress. We rarely if ever stop think "Hey wouldn't it be amazing to leave this wonderful tract of land as it is and work our own existence around it."

Unlike most other occupants of Planet Earth, humans are deeply programmed to modify the environment. Drop a group of naked human beings into a wild place on a mission to survive and their first essentials are clothing, housing, food and water. There is no easy co-existence with nature. We have to change it to survive and more so to attain a degree of comfort. Our pursuit of food entails picking, plucking, digging, planting – and killing.

We are hardwired to exploit our natural environment, to modify it for our own benefit and, in sufficient numbers, to destroy it. And often we do this knowingly. It's as if we have a built in algorithm: if you can't change the climate, you can change the landscape. There is a powerful survival benefit in landscape modification, in agriculture and technology, which means we are unlikely to consciously stop doing those things, even though our survival may now depend on not doing them.

We're not good neighbours with other species. That algorithm wants us to kill nearly everything we encounter. Throughout much of our great migration across the planet, the arrival of humans coincided with the extinction of larger mammals. Giant forms of kangaroo and other marsupials existed in large numbers in ancient Australia but had all gone soon after humans arrived. Woolly mammoths, giant oxen and most of the once vast herds of bison were progressively eliminated from northern Europe and Siberia after the last glacial maximum. Giant camels and horses became extinct in North America and the great herds of buffalo were deliberately decimated right into modern times. The dodo and the passenger pigeon went the same way. These species had no prior experience of humans and were accordingly easy to hunt, so easy that they were hunted to extinction. In Africa by contrast, the human species had emerged alongside indigenous wild mammals and each had formulated its own avoidance and survival strategies over a very long period.

The present day destruction of elephant and rhino populations has been well documented. Less well known is that 99% of Pacific salmon have disappeared through over-fishing and habitat modification. The world population of Right Whales has been hunted to the verge of extinction. There are just a few hundreds left in scattered communities at the extremities of the Atlantic and Pacific oceans. Even their name – 'right' – was coined in recognition they were the 'right' ones to kill. The monarch butterfly, known for its remarkable and spectacular mass migrations between the USA and Mexico, has lost 97% of its numbers in the past 20 years because its food plant, the common milkweed, is being killed off by the widespread use of herbicides. Its overwintering sites are under threat because of people cutting down their preferred trees to build roads, houses and farms.

Cutting down trees is another ingrained habit, though depleting forests seems to take us a little longer than killing off animal populations. America has destroyed 95% of its Pacific Northwest redwood forests. Madagascar has lost 97% of its forest cover. Most of Britain's forests were transformed into ships and buildings a long time ago. I was told of a Kenyan flower farmer who can no longer meet export quality specifications because they cut down nearby forests in order to expand their operations. The local microclimate lost its rainfall and their roses no longer grow properly.

A number of studies have looked at climate change and landscape modification in regard to the the collapse of civilisations. Amongst others, the collapse of the Maya, Khmer and Assyrian societies has been attributed to climatic and environmental factors. In Mesopotamia, sediment evidence shows that around 4,200 years ago, there was a 300-500% increase in wind blown sand, salt and dust which swathed the fields and destroyed the pastures. Forests died back and topsoil washed down the rivers. The drought lasted more than a hundred years and brought the Akkadian empire to a close.

In the remote Pacific Ocean, the inhabitants of Easter Island depended on their indigenous forest for, amongst other purposes, making canoes to go fishing. When the forest was down to its last few trees, the islanders had a choice: preserve them and modify their way of life, or cut them down and seal their doom. They chose the latter.

As territories like USA and Australia were occupied by settlers, indigenous landscapes were bulldozed to make farms in the image of those back home. But the local climate meant that new agricultural practices had to be devised. Huge areas of those landscapes became little more than barren deserts.

More recently, an intense drought between 2007 and 2010 in the Eastern Mediterranean area was the worst for 900 years. Low rainfall drove a steep decline in agricultural productivity and displaced hundreds of thousands of people, mainly in Syria. The IPCC report notes that many historical periods of turmoil have coincided with severe droughts.

Collectively, we've been issuing warnings, signing agreements and consistently ignoring them since the 1972 Stockholm Declaration. The absence of action is laughable. In 1988, James Hansen, then director of the NASA Goddard Institute for Space Studies, told the US Senate: "The greenhouse effect has been detected, and it is changing our climate now." That year was the hottest year since records began, but it has been successively beaten in 1990, 1998, 2010, 2014, 2015, 2016 and 2018. Hansen was right but the Senate chose to ignore him.

Margaret Thatcher espoused the climate bandwagon in a 1992 speech, but backtracked when she realised the implications for capitalism. The Rio Declaration repeated the earlier 'commitments', and that same year the Kyoto Protocol obliged member states to reduce greenhouse gas emissions. But we went on to emit more since then than we ever had before. In 2015, 195 countries adopted the first legally binding agreement to limit global warming to well below 2°C. Russia and Iran (amongst others) refused to ratify and the USA later pulled out.

Tim Flannery warned in 2005 that if the world didn't take decisive action with a decade we'd be in trouble. We didn't, and we are.

Chapter 8

THE BURNING ISSUES

The evidence and the analysis has identified a long list of issues we need to face up to, issues that are putting our existence as a civilisation, if not as a species, at risk. The reports and warnings I've shared highlight how our modern civilisation is under threat from fossil fuel emissions, land use changes, loss of wilderness and wildlife, pollution and waste on an enormous scale. But as we've seen, there is no single cause and therefore no single solution. Multiple problematic trends have converged simultaneously. And many solutions need to be devised and enacted quickly.

In this section, I want to highlight the ultimate causes and the worst offenders so that when we come to suggest some solutions, the links are clear to see. But I keep saying it's complicated: it is. The causes and effects weave together in an ever increasing tangle. Undoing the knots will be equally difficult.

The path of human development that led to where we are started with that revolution in the manufacture of comforts and consumer goods in the Derwent Valley 250 years ago. Improvements in the production of clothing and foodstuffs, coupled with advances in transport, heating and lighting, indisputably improved our lives. Progress in science and technology helped with our battle against disease and infirmity. It enabled us to do and to experience many things that were previously impossible. No-one paused to question that this was a Good Thing. But it's hard to argue that our lives truly have more meaning and value because we can watch TV, chat on our phones, and drive cars at 70mph. That lying on a foreign beach is 'better' than walking in the hills. That living in suburban estates is more rewarding than tending a smallholding. That we need a new sofa every few years, or new toys for the kids every birthday. Sometimes it seems we have come to define our entire existence in terms of the things we buy, or to use an economist's term, things we 'consume'.

Making all those things has brought us to the edge. Manufacturing and transport consume energy, so the use of fossil fuels to power that consumer society has continued to grow. More fuel burned, more things made and shipped. More goods in the shops, more consumption, more fuel burned. The cycle goes on. It's hard, therefore, to say whether energy use is the primary cause of climate change and environmental degradation, or if it's the growth in the population and in consumption. They are inextricably intertwined. The manufacture and distribution of consumer goods also produces pollution and waste which add to the problems of both climate and environment.

The greatest use of fossil fuels is in the oil and gas industry itself, in construction, transport and electricity generation. The use of concrete in construction is so widespread that cement production – highly energy intensive – now contributes 5% of CO_2 production. China's booming construction industry alone produces 3%. The world uses over two billion tonnes a year, and by 2050, concrete use is predicted to reach four times the 1990 level.

All this so-called progress gave us a more comfortable life and, through another complex set of causes and effects, enabled the world's population to grow and grow. The world's population in 1770 at the start of the Industrial Revolution was 800 million. Now it's 8,000 million, ten times more. It's doubled since the mid 70s. Economists and politicians discovered that 'growth' was the recipe for their success. More people, more consumption: it's another positive feedback loop. All those people needed places to live, so towns and cities and roads linking them have also grown exponentially. They need food, which has to be grown and produced. These are the major causes of land use change, switching from natural habitats to serving the desires of the people.

Land use change, especially deforestation, is the second biggest cause of climate change after fossil fuels. The rate of forest loss has doubled since 2003 and the deforestation of tropical rainforests has doubled since 2008. Not only does this reduce the absorption of CO_2 from the atmosphere, it also releases accumulated CO_2 from the forest's soils, a double whammy. The biggest offenders are those who turn over land to burger beef ranches and palm oil plantations. In Costa Rica, 60% of the country's forests have been replaced by cattle ranches that produce 85,000 tonnes of beef every year. But this is paled by Brazil's forest loss and its annual export of two million tonnes of beef.

At sea, one of the greatest problems is the over-fishing of finite fish stocks, while acidification is making the seas less habitable and killing coral.

The worst offenders

In terms of emissions, China is by far the world's worst culprit, accounting for 26.6% of greenhouse gas emissions. The USA follows at 13.1%, and India at 7.1%. Russia accounts for 4.6%, Japan 2.9% and Brazil 2.4%. Iran, Indonesia, Canada and Mexico are also in the top ten, each less than 2%.

On a per capita basis, the USA takes the top slot, followed by the less populous Australia, Canada and Holland.

In terms of waste, the USA tops the league table, followed by Russia, Japan, Germany and the UK.

The greatest loss of primeval forest is in Brazil, the Congo and Indonesia. But that is in part because many other parts of the developed world, including the UK and much of continental Europe, destroyed their own natural forests and woodlands long ago.

The UK takes the overall prize for its cumulative emissions since it started to plunder its coal reserves back in the seventeenth century.

Elephants in the room

Although little substantive action has yet to be taken by governments, climate change has been elevated rapidly towards the top of the public agenda. Many more people are aware of the issues and the threats. Now I want to talk about a few things no-one seems to be facing up to. We know they're there, but for all kinds of reasons, no-one is talking much about them. They're my 'elephants in the room'. And they have the power to lead us inexorably down the road to ruin that many forecasters gloomily predict.

US AND THEM

The first is what I call 'Us and Them'. In Britain and in the wider EU, we are at least talking about some of the kinds of action that need to be taken: reducing greenhouse gas emissions, switching from fossil fuels to renewables, banning single use plastics, introducing electric cars. On their own they are not enough, but something is being done. I suspect we also recognise – reluctantly – that our consumer lifestyle has to change. We are the 'Us'. We kickstarted the problem with our industrial revolution and we seem to recognise we need to take responsibility and do something about it. But that era of industrialisation coincided with our age of expansionist empire, with European powers colonising, occupying and exploiting other countries as far afield as Australia, India, much of Africa, and the Americas. It is not unreasonable that people in this so-called 'developing' world aspire to the same kind of luxury lifestyle they've seen us enjoying. If we include China in the list of aspirants, the peoples of these countries account for more than 70% of the world's still growing population. So here's the catch: who is going to tell all these people they've got to scale back their ambitions and learn to live with what they've got, that becoming 'developed' is no longer an option? Their own governments will certainly do no such thing. And here's a related catch: even if the remaining 30% get serious and do act on the scale required to halt and reverse the damage to the planet, is it really likely we can achieve the global scale of agreement and action that is necessary with the 70% refusing to get on board? Many governments openly espouse policies of environmental destruction in pursuit of short term economic and political gain. They seem to feel that plantations and cities are better for the world than virgin forest. I suppose they're simply following our lead.

POPULATION

My second 'elephant' is Population. It's hard to tell people to stop breeding, especially when their genes and their religious leaders urge them to do the opposite. But every single problem I've highlighted so far is made worse by an increasing population. Amongst the research, the issue of population is brushed off with the observation that it has not yet outstripped global food production. We can feed everyone. Ahem, sorry, that's not the point. The world's population has grown exponentially, and like that of lemmings or locusts it is statistically certain it will crash at some point. Meanwhile, governments love population growth. It facilitates economic growth and paints them in a good light. It drives an increase in tax collections, it necessitates an increase in construction projects, and generally gives the illusion that we're on a roll. But the evidence is that that growth enriches a tiny few at the top at the expense of a large many at the bottom. Economically, socially and biologically, it's not sustainable. The biggest problem with population is really simple. The more people there are to feed and to house, the more the existing problems of emissions, land use change and habitat loss will continue. The population passed 7bn in 2011. In 2019 it's around 7.7bn. By 2030 when the full effects of global warming will be felt, it's going to be around 9bn. Between now and then – a mere ten years – that means finding space for a thousand new cities the size of London or New York. This is not just serious, it is by far the most serious of all the impossible problems we face. And no-one has any realistic suggestions how to tackle it.

GROWTH

Population growth is a disaster, however you look at it. But the world's entire economy is built upon the notion of growth. If a country's economy doesn't grow, it is considered to be in recession. Countries in frequent recession are frowned upon by the international financial community. Those in constant recession are called basket cases or failed states. No wonder hardly anyone is talking about the need to develop a non-growth-based economic model for the future. But for thousands of years, human populations didn't grow very much or very fast. There may have been around 200 million people in the world at the time of the Roman Empire. Five hundred million by the time of the Industrial Revolution and the age of empires. But growth is what enables interest to be paid on savings accounts, dividends to be earned on stocks and shares, profits to be made in business. A bigger pool of people is what enables athletics records to be continually broken, innovations to be hatched up, and, perhaps paradoxically, it correlates with improvements in living standards. This is why few are saying that growth is a bad thing and that the planet cannot stand much more of it.

You only have to look at old maps to see what growth does to land use. When Julius Caesar invaded Britain in the year 55, London was just a crossing place on the River Thames. At the time of the great fire of London in 1666, the capital encompassed only the modern City plus Westminster on the northern bank. Now the continuous urban area of Greater London extends to more than 150 sq miles, roughly a circle some fifty miles in diameter. New York's Manhattan Island was founded as a trading post in 1624. It's now the most densely populated part of the USA with a population of 1.7 million, and a total of 8 million spread across the greater New York state.

There are now 33 'mega-cities' with more than ten million people, and hundreds with more than a million. Most are in Asia. The UN projects that two thirds of the world's people will live in cities by 2030. Is it just me, or is it obvious that there has to be a limit to all this expansion, this exchange of natural spaces for asphalt and concrete? I don't know if anyone is publicly working on a global limit to urbanisation and population. It may not matter. Nature will do what it needs to do anyway.

A WORLD WITHOUT WORK

With more people concentrated into bigger agglomerations, the question arises as to what people will do with their time, with their lives. Conventional employment, as we've known it since the Industrial Revolution, is already waning. Many people operate their own businesses, although often in a subsistence mode, and young people are already wondering what their own futures hold. Large scale industrial and commercial employers have been globalised away from British shores and the public service including health care and education now account for the largest proportion of formal employment in the UK. The welfare system has been criticised for essentially paying people to stay at home and have children. This is a big elephant that wins no votes and therefore is unlikely to be addressed. What kind of caring government would allow children to suffer because their parents are unemployed? But how sustainable is it to pay people simply to live and breed? If it's already difficult to imagine a world without work as we know it, how much more challenging will it be under the various climate change scenarios? Politicians especially will find it hard to accept publicly that the actions they need to take will affect people's jobs and employment prospects. The inevitable shifts in society, coupled with recurring influxes of migrants, will continue to exacerbate these problems.

AMERICA AND CHINA

Talking of America brings me to my next elephant, a pair of them actually. This time it's not that no-one is talking about them, but that they represent probably the biggest threat to climate change salvation. China and the USA are the largest contributors to greenhouse gas emissions and to most of the other primary causes we've examined. Both seem to lack much inclination to do anything about it. Their sponsorship of natural resource depletion and changes in land use is literally world class. It is regrettably a realistic prospect that some parts of the world will try to act sensibly, if too little too late, but that these giants will plough along on their blinkered path to self-destruction as if there is no alternative. Meanwhile China has for several years been on a global spree of acquisition of rights to minerals and natural resources – and the logistics to ship them all home – all over the world.

Fossil fuels also confer military might. Coal drove the colonialist expansion and oil enabled wars to be won. It's hard to imagine self-proclaimed superpowers like America, China and Russia giving up their very sources of power. Nor even lesser states like Israel and Iran who feel threatened.

LEADERSHIP, LACK OF

Which brings me to my next elephant, which is leadership, or the lack of it. Politics and convoluted decision making, coupled with the law of unintended consequences, are partly to blame for bringing us to where we are. The world's systems of government seem substantially incapable of taking the kind of courageous decisions and committing to the collective actions that are now needed. By dint of bad luck, we seem to be living through an era of bad governance and poor leadership (this being the era of Trump, Putin and Brexit). Democracy will only get us out of the mess if we quickly mobilise the vast majority of people to demand action, and to support leaders who are committed to action. But voters tend to vote in their own perceived short term interests. Corporations are wedded to the status quo. Governments live from election to election and, for the time being, lack vision and courage. And the United Nations, far from acting as a global government, is a membership organisation of national vested interests.

Leadership and decision making structures go hand in hand. And too many parts of the world place human need – and sometimes human greed – above all else. Some of my stories highlight the case of Kenya as an avatar for all that's going bad even though it's not the only nor the worst culprit. But that country's conscious, clear and predictable loss of natural habitat and the wildlife that attracts tourists, creates jobs, and is a major contributor to GDP, suggests that something about people, leaders and governance is seriously askew. Tanzania seems to be going the same way.

The Selous Game Reserve is one of Africa's last remaining wilderness areas. But in 2019, a fleet of trucks and bulldozers arrived in the park primed to flatten an area of woodland the size of Surrey and to construct a huge dam across the landmark Stiegler's Gorge through which runs the Rufiji River. It will be one of the world's largest dams, built with the aid of China, in a UNESCO World Heritage Site. Elephant populations have already been under pressure from poaching. You can guess the probability of their survival under the new onslaught. It's hard to know if the

Tanzanian government is proud or embarrassed. They've threatened to lock up anyone who resists the project.

The wild places of Africa may have the most to lose but there are similarly blinkered and destructive processes going on all over the world.

ACTIVE RESISTANCE

Who has the most to lose? Who is sitting on the biggest oil and gas reserves? Whose wealth stands to be diminished in a zero emissions scenario? The top ten, in order: Venezuela, Saudi Arabia, Canada, Iran, Iraq, Kuwait, United Arab Emirates, Russia, Libya, the USA. The next five: Nigeria, Kazakhstan, China, Qatar, Brazil. These are not the countries we expect to see onside in the quest for change. You tell me if you think of these places for their good planetary neighbourliness.

As for the corporations that make money from extracting and burning fossil fuels, the top ten are: Saudi Aramco, Chinese Sinopec, China National Petroleum Corporation, ExxonMobil, Royal Dutch Shell, Kuwait Petroleum Corporation, BP, Total (France), Lukoil (Russia), and Eni (Italy). Tell me if you think these businesses will readily, rapidly and voluntarily write off the enormous asset value of the unburnt hydrocarbons on their balance sheets. Financial assets to them, economic assets to their host countries, one giant liability to mankind.

The UK, by the way, extracted 39 billion BOE (barrels of oil equivalent) of crude oil and natural gas from the North Sea between the 1960s and the early part of the present century. Production peaked in 1999. But in 2018, according to the Oil & Gas Authority, production rose to 1.09 million barrels per day, up 8.9% on the previous year, attributed to more than 30 new fields coming on stream. So much for bragging about renewables.

There is already some evidence that fake news games are being played, as the tobacco industry did with lung cancer. The oil and gas lobby is known to have funded disinformation campaigns, and the White House has been accused of suppressing scientific reports under both Bush and Trump presidencies.

But some of the responsibility lies with us as consumers of energy. A further example of a positive feedback loop helps explain a major dilemma in slowing energy use, or even in gaining the benefit of greater efficiencies. The more energy we've used, the more we use, and the more new sources we find to use. Improvements in efficiency don't seem to lead to reductions in use, but rather to our finding more and more ways to burn more and more fuel. At present rates of growth in energy consumption we will be using twice as much as we do now − let alone reducing it − by 2050. It will be really hard to break this vicious cycle.

ONE LAST ELEPHANT

There are rather more elephants in this crowded room than I expected. Every one of them gives pause for thought. But there's one more. This one's to do with physics and the earth's orbital stability. Something even the scientists do not seem to have talked about is the change of weight distribution as polar ice melts, turns to water and spreads across the planet's oceans. This may, sooner or later, change the way the earth wobbles on its axis. If my reasoning is right, it would tend to speed it up, meaning that the 26,000 year precessional cycle might reduce a bit. Like I said, it's probably a long term phenomenon. But greater mass at the equator might tend to slow down the earth's daily rotation, leading to longer days. You can tell the earth is already somewhat unstable from the way the sun appears to swing back and forth over the seasons. Its axis is 23° off vertical.

The earth's magnetic field is changing, and the location of the magnetic pole is moving. Flipping the poles has happened before. And this, as well as changes in sunspot activity, also has significant effects on the climate. I'm not trying to be more of a scaremonger than necessary here, just pointing out the complexity and uncertainty of all these various causes and effects.

Chapter 9

EXPLODING SOME MYTHS

There is a lot of fake news around the issue of climate change and its potential solutions. In this section, I shall expose and explain some of them.

1: THE MYTH OF CLIMATE CHANGE

Let's start with the naysayers, the climate change deniers. Perhaps surprisingly, apart from the annoying messages from the President of the USA, most people seem to have come around to accepting the reality of climate change. I am, however, occasionally asked "Do you believe in climate change, then?" My response is usually something along the lines of "It's not a matter of belief." I hope the evidence presented in this book makes that clear. But you do also see 'news' items posted claiming that such and such dissident scientist disagrees with the 97% who put their names to the various warnings, or that the former chairman of Greenpeace (or whatever) now disagrees with his or her previous position. You cannot easily tell if these stories are fake. But let's assume that there is a handful of half way credible people who do disagree with the majority. I've seen just two reasons stated for such disagreement. One that climate change is happening but it's not due to human activity. Two that the admittedly complex science is somehow faulty and the data doesn't point to a looming disaster after all. Even if these points of view were valid, however, it doesn't change the in-your-face observation that something is amuck. Even if you attribute changes in the climate to long term cycles or to changes in solar radiation, the effects are still there for us all to see. Even if we were to put the climate issues to the side for a moment, the equally, if not more, disturbing issues of deforestation, pollution, waste and species extinction are still alarmingly real.

Although you might question the science of average temperature calculations, the effect of CO_2 on ocean acidity is quite independent from its role as a temperature raising greenhouse gas.

It is true, however, that historic shifts in global temperatures have bounced from up to down and vice versa in a short space of time. So in all honesty we cannot forecast precisely that the present trend will continue or that it may contrarily slip into reverse. We can however be sure that something bad is going on and that if we do not take action all the terrible events set out in this book will indeed come to pass. Even if they don't in your part of the world, the kind of actions we need to take make sense anyway for social, economic and ethical reasons.

2: THE MYTH OF CLEAN ENERGY

It's a myth that there is any such thing as 'clean' energy. The British government celebrated a week without burning coal in power stations for the first time since the start of the Industrial Revolution. It's a major milestone in the move away from fossil fuels, they say. That is true enough. But most of our electricity generation is powered by natural gas. We were told once upon a time that natural gas was 'clean energy'. Burning it produced no noxious by-products, only water vapour and carbon dioxide. But natural gas is a fossil fuel, and that 'clean' H_2O and CO_2 are greenhouse gases that are killing us.

Wind, waves and sunshine are natural sources of energy which seem (for the time being) to be inexhaustible. Anything you can do with these, you get pretty much for free, and its use shouldn't damage the wider planet. But if you pass them through the supply chain of photovoltaic cells or turbines to create electricity then you incur an energy cost for the manufacture of those devices. There is even a school of scientific thought that nuclear power is an environmentally friendly option. Rather than argue a complex case, I will simply refer you to Dr David Mackay's seminal work 'Sustainable Energy – without the hot air'. He concludes that there is insufficient scope for renewables to fully replace our current, let alone projected, needs.

Meanwhile, the best plan is to reduce your energy consumption wherever possible. There is no viable strategy that does not include this. Electricity is being encouraged as the best option, but you need to be sure it's coming from so-called renewable sources. And here's a couple of things about electric motors for cars, touted as an urgent replacement for the internal combustion engine. The technology for practical day to day use at affordable prices is nowhere near sufficiently developed. And the lithium used in making their batteries is in finite supply. It's 'ownership' may lead to the same kind of cartels we've seen with oil and gas.

3: THE MYTH THAT THERE'S TIME TO SORT IT OUT

Much about the climate, evolutionary change and human history seems to take place over thousands if not hundreds of thousands of years. Doesn't it seem reasonable that the present wave of changes will also take a long time? One response to this is: even if the predicted disasters don't take place in your own lifetime, is this a good reason to deny them, or to fail to take action? But another response is: don't put your trust in time. In an earlier chapter, I described how the climate has previously shifted enough to disrupt human life with a few years. The most telling evidence is that of the woolly mammoths and cave bears of Siberia whose carcasses are now emerging from the melting tundra. One day as they browsed on the Siberian steppe, it snowed and froze and didn't thaw for thirty thousand years.

Change can happen fast. And drought kills as rapidly as does ice. When people say we have until 2030 or 2050 or 2100, ignore them. There is no one predictable moment when things will suddenly shift. It's a process. And it has already started.

4: THE MYTH OF A 'LOW CARBON ECONOMY'

From what we've seen of the problems, trivialising them into a concept like this will not get us very far very fast. A number of cities and organisations have set the goal of becoming 'carbon neutral' by a certain future date. That's good. But it ain't nowhere near enough. And most dates are set so far into the future as to be rather meaningless given the scale of our problems and the urgency of need.

5: THE MYTH OF NET ZERO EMISSIONS

This word 'net' worries me. It implies that some emissions will always be inevitable, and that's surely dangerous. But rather more worrying is that replacing all our fossil fuels with renewable sources of energy seems a distant dream and a logistical nightmare which would need us to cover huge areas of the country (and of other countries) with solar panels and wind turbines. It's a great goal to set, but as yet there is no credible plan to achieve it. As I've noted elsewhere, there is not enough scope for renewable energy sources to fully replace fossil fuels at our present and forecast rates of consumption. Worrying.

6: THE MYTH OF CARBON TRADING

Carbon trading means carrying on producing greenhouse gas emissions while paying someone else to cut theirs. The trade off is supposed to add up to a net reduction in CO_2 pumped into the atmosphere. But I'm sceptical, for the same kind of reasons as I dislike the financial engineering that led to the 2008 collapse. Secondary, derivative, financial markets are a zero-sum game, that is you can only win if someone else loses, and I fear that carbon trading is in the same league. There is also that law of unintended consequences. In May 2019, British Steel, a last vestige of a once powerful industrial sector, was placed into receivership. It was bankrupt, 25,000 jobs under threat. It was reported that a contributory factor was a £100 million government loan to pay into the EU emissions trading system.

7: THE MYTH THAT WE CAN OFFSET OUR 'CARBON FOOTPRINT'

What does this mean, honestly? Words and phrases like 'offset', 'footprint', 'carbon trading' and 'carbon credits' have crept into the jargon of pseudo-climate action. You may have been offered the option when booking a flight to 'offset' your emissions by paying a certain amount of money. The EU's emissions trading system allows industrial polluters to buy, trade or use carbon credits to pay for their emissions. Each credit gives a company the right to emit a tonne of carbon dioxide. So tell me, how does a payment for an emissions-laden activity help to reduce the impact? The 'theory' is that the trading scheme passes on funds to people and projects in other parts of the world that is intended to incentivise them not to cut down forests (for example) or to set up programmes related to ameliorating negatives impacts in some way. There are two problems with this. One, it doesn't work. Two, it's a drop in the ocean of negative trends that barely registers a blip on the continuing slide into global disaster. As we've noted elsewhere, the scale of habitat loss and deforestation continues to increase not decrease. Also, I find it rather patronising. Rich world carries on polluting while assuaging its guilt by channeling funds to the poor world in the hope they won't follow suit.

8: THE MYTH OF CARBON CONTENT LABELLING

This was an idea put to me in all seriousness. Make it mandatory that every single product be labelled with its carbon contribution. I mean, without that knowledge, how can we make informed buying choices? Good point. But I foresee a couple of problems. One is the total absence of a point of comparison. If something is labelled 0.25kg or ml or whatever, is that good or bad? How about 15.8? Or 102? Or should it be more like ingredients in health supplements measured in micrograms? Which brings me to the second point: few people take much note of existing labelling requirements on, for example, processed foods. And in any case manufacturers play games to make sure that 'sugar' (for example) is listed as sucrose, sucralose, fructose, glucose and other '-oses' so it doesn't appear at the top of the list. You can't trust product labelling, unfortunately. But it's still a good idea. Information is better than ignorance.

9: THE MYTH OF NEW TECHNOLOGICAL SOLUTIONS

There is no doubt that there is a role for innovative technological approaches for solving climate change and related issues. Indeed I am certain that the pursuit of solutions will stimulate such innovations. However, some of the ideas currently being talked about are rather too fanciful for comfort. One is to seed the atmosphere above the poles to create clouds which reflect sunlight and restore the effect of the lost ice. Another is to suck carbon dioxide out of the atmosphere and store it underground. Such concepts are far more complicated than dreaming up ways of reducing current emissions and tackling other causes directly. They are attractive precisely because they do not challenge the status quo of dirty manufacturing and excessive resource extraction. In fact, they will demand investment orders of magnitude greater. Yet nearly every so-called zero emissions plan includes a plea for technological solutions that do not yet and may never exist. Settlements on the Moon and on Mars are in the same league of fancy. It's far simpler to adjust to a new life on earth than to create one from scratch on another world. But even those technologies that form part of current plans, for example electric cars and carbon sequestration, are far from developed as practical solutions.

10: THE MYTH THAT THERE'S ENOUGH FOOD TO GO ROUND

There is and there isn't. So long as you are content just to stay alive on processed and packaged maize or soy flour (or whatever other genetically modified crop is on offer), then yes the numbers add up. For the time being. But the big producers are in North America and Russia and the greatest consumer need is in Africa and Asia. The real problem with plantation based mass food production is the depletion of nutrients from the soil. These have to be replaced with fertiliser manufactured from, wait for it, crude oil. Soil depletion is a vicious cycle, a positive feedback loop. The worse it gets, the worse it gets. Food quantity may be sufficient, food quality is not. Not now, and not in the future. It's a direct threat to health quite separate from those we've already enumerated here.

11: THE EQUALITY MYTH

Several authors have suggested that climate change is unfair. It hits the poorest the hardest. Whilst it is true that bodies like the United Nations have the alleviation of poverty and inequality amongst their 'sustainable development goals', I fear this rather diverts attention from the issue at hand. The climate has no favourites. Whether you own a sea front condominium in Miami Beach or a meagre blanket in Juba, hurricanes and droughts will hit you just the same. The climate is a great leveller. The rich and the comfortable have the most to lose. Jared Diamond explained long ago that it was the happenstance of geography and climate that favoured some people in some places, and not others. That is still the case. In the worst case, I suspect the few remaining hunter-gatherers on the planet might come out on top.

12: THE MYTH THAT THE GOVERNMENT WILL BALE US OUT

Under the radar, some governments do quite a lot for their people. But they seem to find it hard to tackle big long term issues, and fundamental change is quite beyond them. Personally I don't have much trust in governments. They are too big, too arrogant, too self-enriching. And, we expect too much of them. In the UK it has been observed that their leaders always end in failure. So far as I can see, they've messed up housing, transport, eduction, health and law and order. And that's without much thinking. Maybe I'm just a sceptic.

13: THE MYTH THAT THERE'S NO POINT ACTING ALONE

I saw a comment from Australia that if they halted the burning of all fossil fuels, it would only add up to 3% of the world's emissions, so why bother? Well that's the whole point of international cooperation, no one country alone can save the planet and save humanity. It requires concerted global action. You know, the thing that Antonio Guterres is saying isn't happening. If every country fails to act, even if many fail to act, then we are sealing our doom. Therefore everyone has to act, even if, to start with, it feels like we're alone.

14: THE MYTH THAT IT'S BEYOND ME

On which note, individual action is perhaps the most important. Every single problem we've discussed is the result of the sum of individual actions. If every individual were to take action, we wouldn't need to rely on hopeless governments and failing global decision making. I'll set out what we all need to do in another chapter.

15: THE MYTH THAT THIS IS AN ANTI CAPITALIST LEFT WING PLOT

The challenges of climate change dwarf party politics such that left-right, in-out, red-blue are largely meaningless. We Brits living through the Brexit mess just wish the entire edifice of political parties with their self-interest, posturing and adversarial style could just disappear. I'm sure citizens of many countries feel much the same for their own reasons. However, as we've seen, there seems little doubt that large scale manufacturing, industrialisation and the capitalist financed market system have been complicit in, if not a direct cause of, the mess we find ourselves in. It also seems that short term democratic systems of government may not be up to the job of getting us out of it. We've noted that unlimited growth – for the planet at least – is a Bad Thing. So this might all seem a bit liberal lefty. Already journalists have accused climate activists of terrorism and scaremongering and wanting to throw the economy into recession.

So what? If to achieve a new dispensation in the way we live our lives requires a similarly new way of governing, then so be it. Let's add it to the 'to-do' list.

16: THE MYTH THAT WE'RE BEING TOO PESSIMISTIC

Go back and re-read the earlier chapters. Wishful thinking doesn't make it go away. Like I've said already, I'm sorry.

Chapter 10

A POST CONSUMER SOCIETY

No-one seemed to think we would hit the earth's carrying capacity within a single lifetime. After the dreadful slaughter of the first half of the 20th century, growth, compared to warfare and disease, seemed like a positively good idea. We'd never had it so good. Never had such value been placed on human life, on maintaining it and on extending it. But faced with the threats to our civilisations, our communities and our lives, we now need to redefine what 'good' means and live it differently.

There was a time when people who cared for the environment were snubbed as 'tree-huggers'. When people who lived off grid were derided as 'hippies'. But now to be 'green' is not only fashionable, it's essential. So in this section of the book I'm setting out some of the things about life that need to change. The chapter's title might suggest that I'm promoting an anti-capitalist agenda. But it's becoming rather evident that facing up to the causative issues we've identified will require transformation in many aspects of our capitalist-funded, market-driven, consumer society. Major change is never achieved by doing the same things in the same ways.

And social change must be on the agenda. Back in the day, Arkwright's mill set off an industrial revolution. But his on-site housing scheme for workers and his terms of employment caused a social revolution. Just five years later, Adam Smith set in train free market capitalism with the publication of his 'Wealth of Nations', the first modern work on economics. So if easing into our modern consumer lifestyle involved an industrial, technological, social and economic revolution, then easing out of it will too.

We've talked extensively about the need to reduce emissions but in reality this is a proxy for reducing energy use. In turn, energy correlates with consumption. As a country's economy develops, so its per capita energy consumption increases. To have any hope of getting close to zero harmful emissions, our use of energy has to slow, stop or change considerably. So let's talk a bit about energy. In the UK, per capita energy use works out to around 200 kWh per day. It goes mainly on motor vehicles, flights, heating and cooling, lighting, food production, transport, gadgets, devices and the 'stuff' of a consumer lifestyle. The majority of this – around 80% – comes from burning fossil fuels, for the most part natural gas, petrol, diesel, paraffin and coal. Although 'biomass' is not a fossil fuel – it's grown specially and therefore counts as a renewable – it is also burnt and produces harmful emissions. Eliminating these emissions means replacing that 80% with energy sources such as solar, wind, and wave power.

Professor David MacKay set out to show if this switch could be achieved in practice. You can download his book free from www.withoutthehotair.com. He concluded that even if vast portions of the country were swathed under solar panels and wind turbines, and even if local communities agreed to have their neighbourhoods thus converted to power production, there would be a shortfall of some 20% at best. This means that the option of continuing our energy guzzling consumer lifestyle, in the hope that a zero emissions solution can be found, is pie in the sky. We have to learn to live with less.

On the positive side, the UK's total emissions have been steadily reducing, by around 38% since 1990, faster than any other major developed country. This is mainly due to 'cleaner' electricity generation based on gas and renewables instead of coal, more efficient fuel consumption by business and industry, reduced electricity use in the industrial and residential sectors, and changes in transport emissions. The British government has announced that Britain would be legally bound to aim for zero net emissions by 2050. But as of now, no-one has any idea how or if this can be done. And in any case, it's too far away to be useful.

If reducing emissions of greenhouse gases to zero means we have to stop burning fossil fuels completely, what will this mean for the economy and for our lifestyles? Imagine fuel prices were to quadruple as they did in 1973 and 1990. Or that geo-political instability around Iran or Russia were to bring supplies to a halt. We would be forced to stop travelling and hunker down. Who recalls the 1973/74 three day week with its power cuts and rationing? Reduced energy also means reducing the manufacturing of consumer goods. Such a scenario is not far removed from what a post-climate change, zero emission, post-consumer society might look like. Every aspect of the economy and of daily life will change. The need for innovation will spur investment and growth in sectors related to renewable energy and the broader use of electric power. But this will be overshadowed by other sectors slowing to a halt: oil and gas, chemicals, some transport, some forms of especially polluting manufacturing, some types of farming and food production. Air travel will most likely be gradually taxed out of reach. The era of cheap flights is over.

One early indicator of likely effects came as the Ford Motor Company announced the closure of its Bridge End engine manufacturing plant in South Wales, attributing its woes to a climate driven shift away from internal combustion engines.

So, how might the present dispensation unravel? At the time of writing, we are already seeing a growing disaffection with party politics and the apparent inability of parliament to make consensus driven decisions. There is a polarisation of opinion across the country on many important issues. Discontent has been evident for some years in regard to employment prospects, cuts to public services, and the apparent disconnect between a London based government and the rest of the country and the needs of its people. High Streets have become characterised by charity shops, betting shops, Vietnamese nail bars and Turkish barbers. Traditional retailers have been going out of business left right and centre. Once magnificent period buildings are occupied by pizza outlets and chain restaurants. Parts of the country have been inundated by devastating floods. New housing estates are being developed on green field sites at the edges of towns and villages all over the country. And large numbers of intelligent people have been taking to the streets to protest.

Immigration – the primary issue which led to the 2016 Brexit referendum – is unlikely to slow. Quite the contrary: migration from war-torn and drought-stricken countries will escalate. Even as people complain that some parts of Britain no longer seem 'British', and that some parts of America speak more Spanish than English, these trends are set to continue. Due to shifts in employment prospects, flood risk and general discontent, some people will choose to relocate their families. A general slowdown in the economy will become prolonged, reducing tax collections at the same time as welfare claims rise. Public service budgets will become ever more constrained, leading to reduced municipal services and compromised health care provision. In turn this will lead to greater activism, especially amongst younger people, greater tensions across society and, to a greater or lesser degree, actual conflict. Even if these trends are most apparent in other parts of the world, we will all feel the ramifications.

By 2030, 20% of the European population will consist of retired 'Baby Boomers'. Europe is already effectively broke, so who is going to pay for their keep? Couple economic and financial constraints to the climatic and environmental woes and it's hard to avoid a strong sense of impending disaster. These trends have the power to reshape society as we know it, or worse cause it to fall apart. We need a sense of urgency. Many proposals and targets have been set with dates of 2040, 2050 or even 2100 on them. It's too easy to delay things beyond our own generation's lifetime. It's lazy, and it's unfair on our kids. In any case, we have to take dramatic immediate action to keep climate change within the currently predicted 2°C rise, let alone the far worse scenarios of 4°C and more.

There are people – me included – who feel these trends are now more or less inevitable. But gloomy though the picture certainly is, society as a whole, and each of us as families and individuals, may be better off for it. The solutions will need to include greater personal responsibility, greater self-reliance, greater mutual respect and tolerance, and a much enhanced sense of community. Challenging though it will certainly be to achieve a post consumer society, it is at least becoming a topic of conversation. And there are some tangible benefits to look forward to: cleaner air, cleaner rivers, quieter streets, tastier and more nutritious foods, greater communal support and a more natural environment with more wildlife closer to home.

What we have to do is simple, so you might think. Stop burning fossil fuels. That's it. Not complicated, is it? But the reality is that the rate at which we're pumping CO_2 into the atmosphere is not only still increasing, it's accelerating. Even as you hear that the UK has reduced its use of coal, 83% of power is still based on burning fossil fuels. Between them, China, India, America, Australia and Indonesia are now burning more coal now than the UK ever did. Can you imagine oil producing companies and nations coming together to agree to leave their valuable resources in the ground? But there isn't another option. Hmmm.

Emissions of damaging greenhouse gases have to stop, not just be reduced progressively. If that means bankrupting the likes of Aramco and the Saudi state (and others), so be it. They're resourceful enough to make another plan. But there are many vested interests – both nations and corporations – who will resist. Governments have to stop subsidising damaging industries. They cannot favour jobs and profits over the planet. They have to actively prevent the destruction of natural habitats and encourage the restoration of those already damaged. The controlled development of homes and urban areas, already a challenge, has to be much more rigorous and much more creative. Killing wild species and over-fishing has to be stopped, don't ask me how. Whatever measures are in place are obviously not working. Perhaps governments should set up departments of future sustainable life to encourage appropriate research, provision of information and funding. The reference point for decision making needs to be the integrity of the environment, not the selfish interests of the electorate or of the politicians themselves. I have no idea how to achieve this.

Governments have a role to play too in obliging companies to stop their constant quest for cost cutting, low prices, higher volumes and greater profits. Company legislation should hold directors responsible for environmental stewardship and not solely for financial performance. Companies must account for their emissions, their waste and their other impacts. They must have concrete programmes in place, not just sweet sounding words in an annual report or an ISO certification. They must design products for longevity, not for obsolescence. Business models should be fair and transparent, not revolving around some opaque form of financial engineering built on insurance. All this will probably require some obligation through legislation.

Cultural practices and personal values may present some of the greatest challenges. It may not seem like a big issue in the UK, but in many parts of the world religion continues to fully guide people's values and behaviours, typically pointing them in a contrary direction, for example by prohibiting birth control and encouraging large families. For many, words like 'development' and 'progress' intuitively imply the destruction of landscapes in favour of concrete and asphalt, perceived as a positive rather than negative act. It exercises my mind to consider how – or if – such deeply entrenched attitudes can be reversed quickly enough.

In fact, it's far from clear if there can be a managed transition to this post consumer society, or if disruptive change is inevitable. Scientists are telling us it's time to adapt to the end of the world as we know it. They know this is a depressing message. They know the public is, by and large, ill-informed, and doesn't care enough to act. They also know that governments are, by and large, ill-equipped to take the necessary actions. But our existing structures lack the appropriate forums for doing this differently. We will need a new form of economics, new structures of government, new ways of living and of working, and a new set of morals and values. And these need to be shared right around the world. There will be winners and there may be losers. Which side you are on is largely a matter of choice. The greatest challenge is to accept that our entire modern comfortable consumer lifestyle has to stop. I would not like to suggest it needs to go into reverse – though it may look like that – but we have to dedicate our most creative resources to devising a collective lifestyle that is less fuel-dependent and less consumer-driven, but essentially of greater meaning and value.

What businesses can do

I've described above some of the things we need our governments to act on: an end to growth, the end of careless capitalism, the end of profit as the primary measure of success. These will be difficult if not impossible challenges. And even if we are able to cut fossil fuel usage and slash emissions, (eg 50% by 2030, 90% by 2050), there is no global movement towards reducing deforestation and habitat loss. But since most emissions are pumped out by businesses, this is a good place to make a difference. There are plenty of things that businesses can do.

Business as we know it, including transport and logistics, has to change. I know there will be great resistance, but it has to be said. Profit at the expense of the planet is no longer acceptable. It's immoral and should be illegal. Imagine tomorrow there will be a fuel shortage, deliveries of raw materials are delayed, and customers can't pay their bills. That's the scenario we're facing. The starting point is to accept that this is not business as usual, it's the new reality. There may be some short term loss of competitiveness for early adopters of the new way, but soon everyone will be in the same boat, at which point you regain advantage because you're ahead of the game. So choose now: do you want to lead or lag the shift that's coming?

I'm setting out below a rational approach you can use, based on my experience of strategy consulting and change leadership. You can find more, including some downloads, on my website www.strategicalignmentltd.com.

1: Redefine purpose and strategy

2: Involve people from inside and outside your business

3: Audit your environmental impacts

These three actions need to be done pretty much at the same time.

The owners of businesses will have little more idea what needs to be done than their employees, suppliers or customers. A collective approach to brainstorming your way forward is essential. Bear in mind too that people individually, their families and communities are in the firing line as much as your business is. Redefining the purpose of your business means moving away from 'simply' filling a need, satisfying a customer demographic, selling a product or service, and making a profit. Operating in the best interests of your people and the planet has to be part of the deal. For many organisations, this may represent an existential shift which threatens the sustainability of the business.

Talking of sustainability – an impossible concept, if you ask me – I want to alert you to the danger of relying on existing programmes which purport to tackle this. Some organisations already put their people through sustainability or resilience training. Some have appointed departments of sustainability with leaders and staff and a budget. This is not the solution, I'm afraid. The actions required to tackle the issues set out in this book demand that everyone gets involved and that a new set of values and operating principles underpin everything everyone does. It cannot be delegated to a 'department for survival'.

I've included the suggestion that businesses carry out an environmental audit to determine where they are currently on a scale of damage to the environment. I know some organisations already do this, to some extent. But simply calculating your so-called 'carbon footprint' is not the point. There are several 'carbon calculators' available online and it can be an entertaining thing to do. But its value is on a par with calculating the weight of bullets fired in Afghanistan (for example): particularly meaningless when you're about to be blown up by an IED. It is of course common sense to read your meters and monitor your energy consumption and you should be doing this anyway.

Some organisations will already be aware of environmental management standards and so-called 'green accreditation' schemes. BSI published BS7750 as long ago as 1992, superseded in 1996 as ISO14000. The newer ISO50000 series covers energy management systems. But these standards, while useful in their own way, do not guarantee your environmental credentials any more than operating to ISO9000 guarantees a high quality product. Standards such as these ensure that you prepare and follow a plan, but they don't specify how that plan truly impacts your operations, or the planet for that matter. They don't go nearly far enough in prompting truly meaningful change.

Here in the Peak District, businesses have access to a reasonably robust 'Environmental Quality Mark' scheme. Check if such a thing is available in your own locality.

I'm sure the government will soon be publishing 'green guidelines' but if their advice on 'Brexit resilience' is anything to go by, they have no more idea than the rest of us. As we've noted earlier, relying on national or international 'carbon trading' and 'green financing' schemes is also counter-productive. As currently designed, they simply allow companies to continue to emit greenhouse gases while paying someone else not to. We can expect much more complex wizardry of this sort to emerge. But I fear that rather like the games played with financial derivatives in the run up to the 2008 financial crisis, these would hasten the environmental crisis. It puts a smoke screen around an actual lack of change.

On the other hand, a pursuit of technological solutions must form part of your on-going strategy. These will include greater use of renewable energy sources, better efficiencies, and the ability to manage energy use. No doubt many other innovations will be driven by the imperative to act. One area in which most businesses can take action is environmentally driven design thinking. A simple example is the design of packaging materials. Some retailers and food producers claim to be reviewing their use of plastics, following revelations they end up killing marine life in the oceans. But packaging design emphasises the preservation and protection of foodstuffs and goods, and this often leads to three or more types of plastic being used in a single pack. On a recent long haul flight I counted twelve different plastics making up the various accoutrements to an in-flight meal. This means that none of it is likely to be recycled.

Indeed many retailers and airlines seem not to know how much of their waste is actually recycled, in spite of published policies that they do so. The use of environmental impact as a reference point may lead to a replacement of complex plastics with paper and other naturally derived materials which are both renewable and biodegradable.

The issue of plastics is complex. I use the term loosely to imply a very wide range of man-made materials, many if not all deriving from crude oil as a feedstock. Everywhere I look around my workspace there is plastic. It has spawned a materials revolution. My desk is plastic (made to look like wood). My speakers, the computer screen and much of its innards. The keys I'm striking. The laminated covers of my books. The printer casing. My camera. The window frames, the doors, the carpet, many of my clothes, my glasses (three types of plastic). Probably 70% of my car is plastic of one sort or another. Even aeroplanes are plastic, including their photochromic windows. Kitchen worktops, waste bins, paint, water bottles, plant pots, key rings, phone cases. The list is endless, and that's just in the home. It's an amazing list of versatile, lightweight, convenient materials. The trouble is, their production entails noxious emissions and their disposal leaves potentially poisonous traces throughout the world's food chain. Mostly, plastics are too complex to recycle. And there's too much of it anyway.

I raise this as an example of how environmental thinking needs to come into design. By all means design for functionality, for appearance, for convenience, and for cost. But also design for impact and disposal. These are killer issues, quite literally.

Finally, be proud of your environmental credentials and don't be afraid to tell people about them. Remember we're trying to create a movement, not keep things secret.

None of these approaches will fully succeed without attitudinal and cultural shifts amongst business owners, shareholders, managers, employees and regulators. And I am quite certain that in some of the world's most powerful boardrooms, there will be strong resistance to anything that threatens their profitable status quo. The coal, oil and gas lobby has collectively held back our understanding and action by decades through disinformation, political lobbying and cash funding to nay-sayers. Of course they will resist: they're about to become unnecessary and irrelevant. The planet can no longer afford their plundering. Already, litigation is playing its part in pinning down responsibility. Court cases in both the USA and Europe are raising the prospect of corporations and perhaps even governments being held to account. Companies, industries and states which have knowingly continued their emissions or which have deliberately sought to subvert opinion could face action from communities whose livelihoods, lifestyles and actual survival have been compromised. The phrase 'crimes against humanity' is being used.

Britain has an unenviable and undeniable role as the perpetrator of the industrial revolution and its export to much of the rest of the world. But it has also been one of the first to take substantive action to reduce the burning of coal and increasing the use of renewables. Equally indisputable is the regrettable laxity of countries such as the USA, Australia and China – and many others – in acknowledging their harm to the planet, in denying the urgent need, and by refusing to take serious action. Brazil has become an embarrassment to the global community for its wanton destruction of its forests. A future, post-apocalyptic world order may choose not to forget these things.

Now we can turn to the actions that individuals – including business owners and their employees – can take.

Chapter 11

ATTITUDES AND ACTIONS

What kind of future do you want for your children? 2030 is the day after tomorrow. You can choose to act now and be an influencer for the new dispensation, or just be carried along by the breaking wave and be washed up on its shore. The risk is that our our children will not have a better life than we did. Human beings individually can be amazing, wonderful, beautiful, clever, creative and kind. But collectively we are a disaster. We have to act now as individuals. It's all down to us. You and me. And people like you and me. We all need to become climate evangelists, advocates for the environment. We can't change the world by ourselves. We can't trust our governments. What we can do is set an example, spread the word and create a movement.

Zero emissions means not playing games with trading and trade offs. It means – quite simply – that we have to stop burning fossil fuels. People will argue that some is inevitable, some is even necessary. In the short term that may be true. But that doesn't change the message. We have to stop burning fossil fuels. All of us, everywhere. Oil, gas, so-called 'biomass', even wood. Everything and anything that goes up in smoke makes the climate worse. In turn this means leaving those still remaining reserves in the ground. That's tricky when the royal families of states as diverse as Brunei and Saudi Arabia have earned their tea ticket with the Queen of England through their oil wealth. It's an odd thing about oil rich nations that they seem mostly to be de facto dictatorships and kleptocracies: Venezuela, Russia, China, Iran, Angola. Oil wealth does relatively little, it seems, for ethics and morality and for the good of ordinary people. So let's assume that such nations, powerful only for reasons of their oil reserves, will prefer to let the planet steam rather than lose their riches. What to do?

Answer: sanctions and boycotts. As individuals, we have a collective power far beyond that of governments. If we simply stop buying their energy and the things it creates, then demand can quickly diminish. We can play OPEC at its own price fixing game. No demand, no value, no supply. I know it's not that simple. But hey, we gotta try, there isn't any option.

Already, many people are becoming involved in community based programmes of action. There are climate coalitions and alliances, climate action groups, transition groups and, if it's your thing, campaigns of direct action and civil disobedience. School strikes and street protests have helped place climate change right at the top of the agenda. The evidence set out in this book implies that a massive and fundamental shift is urgently required in the way we live our lives. This will be difficult for everyone. There is no-one to guide us, no role models, no rules. It's up to you how much change you can adapt to and how quickly. The tips that follow are not in any particular order of importance. And none is more important than any other. It's more a matter of trying to do a lot of things differently all at the same time. Collectively, multiplied by millions of people, it WILL make a difference. It's pretty much the only thing that can.

Here are some figures to help set the context.

The average household in the UK produces 2.7 tonnes of CO_2 per year, mainly from heating and cooking (in the USA it's 7.5 tonnes). We produce a tonne of waste annually. Each person uses an average of 140lit of water every day, which means that a typical household uses more than 200,000 litres a year.

45% of waste is reckoned to be recycled in the UK (it's a lot less in the USA), meaning 55% is not. 90% of plastic is not recycled and 25% of food goes to waste.

In terms of fuel usage for an average car, a litre of petrol burns with about 3lit of oxygen to produce two and a half kilos of CO_2 plus one and a half of water vapour. That means in a year, your car produces more than 2.5 tonnes of destructive CO_2.

Flying is a lot worse. A short haul flight typically generates 250kg of CO_2 per passenger. Long haul, for example London to Johannesburg, around 1.9 tonnes of CO_2 per passenger.

These are shocking figures. We have to disrupt the present dispensation of unconstrained energy use, emissions, pollution, waste, loss of nature and growth. And to do that, we will have to change some habits and espouse some new morals and values some of which are the exact opposite of what we've been accustomed to. Here are some examples of what I mean.

Our lives revolve around earning, buying and discarding in an ever increasing cycle. 'Consuming' seems to have become a habit, a way to fill an otherwise humdrum life whose purpose we can't quite figure out. This has to stop. Stop buying things you don't need, just for the sake of shopping or having something new. If this defines your existence – as it does for many – it's time to realign your life with something more meaningful and less damaging. There is growing evidence that tying our well-being to the acquisition of possessions is harming people's health as well as that of the planet. It's strongly associated with negative emotions and mental health issues such as anxiety, depression, low self-esteem and problems with relationships. We need to learn to think of life as defined by positive relationships and experiences, not by income and bank balance, and less by possessions.

Since the world's massively and still escalating population is a big part of the problem, we have to change our attitudes towards family and children. It's uncaring and irresponsible to have more than two children, and even that's too many. It's not a 'blessing' to have several children or grandchildren as we thought it was, it's a curse on the planet.

Because we have no guidelines for the new world, it will be important to talk to your friends, family, neighbours and workmates and debate a new vision of what makes life good, what to aspire to, what's OK and what's not. For example, it's cool to be green and hug trees, in fact it's disgusting not to.

Businesses have a particular challenge. They can no longer be defined solely by profit and growth but also by a duty of care to people (inside and outside the organisation) and to the environment.

The reference points for this new dispensation will be our contribution to emissions and waste, personal responsibility and self reliance. Although the need to act is urgent and enormous, let's admit we're not going to turn off the heating, sell our cars and cancel our overseas holidays any time soon. So what are the practical things we can do? It's a long list, which just goes to show that there are a lot of things we've been doing wrong.

IN THE HOME

After industry, it's in the home that much of our energy is consumed – for heating, lighting and cooking – and where much of our waste is generated. The advice used to be 'Reduce – Recycle – Reuse'. This is still a good tip but now it needs to go further. I suggest 'Buy Less – Burn Less – Waste Less' as a starting point.

• Don't be wasteful: your rubbish is mostly packaging and food waste, you can reduce both easily by just thinking about what you buy and where you shop.

• Recycle everything you can but don't assume the contents of your recycling bin will be actually recycled: challenge your local authority.

• Take stuff to charity shops and recycling 'banks', but again do some homework on how and whether these various materials actually get recycled as opposed to ending up in a Malaysian rain forest.

• In the long run, cleaner renewable energy will reach the home as electricity, so start switching your appliances from gas and oil as budgets allow.

• In the meantime, get ruthless about switching things off that you don't need, especially heaters and lights. And get all the family to do the same.

• Make sure your roof, walls and windows are insulated. If necessary, get an expert to come and check. Government grants are sometimes available to improve insulation.

• Turn off your taps and don't let water flow away: almost certainly you don't need the 140 litres a day average. Don't leave taps running while you're brushing your teeth, for example. Get everyone in the family to make this a habit.

- The disposal of cosmetics and beauty products is a major problem. Try to reduce the amount, and whenever possible, go for natural materials.

- Watch your laundry habits and run your wash only when you need to, with full loads. Household laundry is a major source of waterborne pollution, the effluent being laden with detergents and millions of microscopic plastic particles from your clothes. If you have the space, dry your clothes on a rack in the air rather than run a dryer.

- The manufacture of materials for the construction of houses is a major contributor to greenhouse gas emissions, so if you are in a position to do so, carry out some research and buy property that is presented as more 'eco-friendly'. Bricks, concrete and steel are amongst the worst offenders, which is why wood based materials are coming into favour. Wood is made of carbon, it stores it rather than releasing it.

WHAT YOU EAT

The use of large areas of land for growing crops and rearing livestock is one of the greatest contributors to deforestation. Beef is particularly bad for the environment, in part because cattle produce methane from their ruminant digestive system. Beef production may be the single most climate destructive food there is. Burgers and steaks kill wildlife, sorry. But so too do tropical plantation crops like palm oil, tea, cocoa, pineapples and bananas. Transporting foods around the globe is another major source of greenhouse gas emissions. It would help persuade those who produce such foodstuffs to switch strategy if we consumed less meat and less in the way of processed foods.

- Eat less meat, favour free range pork and poultry.
- Prefer natural foods that are produced locally whenever possible.
- Don't buy ready made snacks and meals, make your own.
- Eat more vegetables and fruit, it's more healthy anyway.
- Learn where your foods come from and what goes into them.
- Reduce your food waste.

SHOPPING

There are people who choose to support a 'go minimalist' movement. It's not for everyone but it's a sound idea. The one overriding action we can all take to face up to the threats to the climate and the environment is to stop being an unconscious consumer. Just stop buying things you don't need. Prefer products with long life built in and replace them less often (eg TVs, washing machines, phones). There is no reason why such things cannot last fifteen or twenty years, or indefinitely. Their failure in three or four years, and the offer of guarantees and maintenance contracts to fix them is a business model (a 'ruse') to optimise profits.

- Don't buy new clothes and cosmetics so often.
- Buy clothes (and other things) made from natural materials whenever possible.
- If shopping is a habit or a pastime, take pride in coming home with empty bags and just enjoy the experience.

- Buy only the things you really need, don't let life become a spree of acquisition for things you'll have to get rid of some day. If you've ever had to clear a house, you will know just how much 'stuff' we accumulate.

- Avoid single use plastics.

- Try to avoid buying things wrapped in multiple complex plastics.

- Re-use your shopping bags time and time again.

- Shop in local shops run by local traders selling locally produced products wherever possible. It helps support your own community and it helps reduce costs and emissions associated with long distance freight.

- Try to avoid instant gratification deliveries. The jury is out as to whether the carbon cost of home delivery is more or less than for personal shopping expeditions, but doing without for longer is definitely the better option.

- Beauty and hygiene products and cosmetics are a big problem, from raw materials to manufacture to their effect on your skin and to disposal. Try to go easy on them.

- Get things fixed rather than replacing them.

CLOTHING

This one is difficult. Many if not most clothes are made from man-made fibres, which means to say plastics of one sort or another. But then again it seems that the plantations that produce cotton, and the amount of water used to transform it into fabric, also stack up badly on their environmental impacts. Microscopic plastic particles from laundering clothes are a major source of pollution and a carcinogenic risk throughout the food chain. Even so, we can suggest some sensible approaches.

- Favour natural products in general, though you may have to scour the labels with a magnifying glass to determine exactly what things are made of.

- Extend the life of your clothes by buying better quality in the first place and keeping in use for longer.

- Consider charity shops as places to both buy and dispose.

TRAVEL AND TRANSPORT

The movement of people and goods around the world is one of the greatest uses of energy and one of the most serious causes of airborne and waterborne pollution. As with many other action areas, we have to learn to do less of it. It's a major contributor to climate change and, when you factor in the vast infrastructure of ports, highways and everything that goes into it, it's also a big contributor to habitat loss. Ships and trucks and planes are amongst the worst emitters of greenhouse gases.

- Shorten or stop your commute – live near your work, work near your home, or work from home. As someone who has worked from home for many years, after previously commuting in and out of London every day, I can assure you that travelling to and from your place of work is a waste of time, a waste of money, and it's bad for the environment.

- Motor vehicles are one of the big problem areas and we can expect to see major changes in how we use them. Get ahead of the curve and learn about fuel efficiency, low emission, and electric options.

- Drive less, drive more slowly, never ever leave your engine idling.

- Use trains and buses, share cars.

- Walk or bike, it's more healthy anyway.

- Flying is a big contributor to greenhouse gas emissions. If you live under a busy airway, you will have seen con trails criss-crossing the sky, sometimes to the extent that these man-made clouds affect the amount of sunlight reaching the ground. Take a look at the FlightRadar24 app and see for yourself just how many planes there are in the air at any one time. Where on earth are all these people going? And what for? On top of that, airports and their access routes take up huge areas of land. For those running airlines, safety and service issues are making it ever harder to make a profit and stay in business. We can expect something of a shake up in aviation, I suspect, especially if we all choose to travel less, which is what this tip is really recommending. Become a 'Less Frequent Flyer'.

- Holidays and overseas travel are always going to be important, so let's not get too carried away with this one. But then again, there are plenty of options closer to home that involve less travelling and less hassle. I just did a trip to a country that speaks a foreign language, has an intriguing culture and great scenery, doesn't require a visa and doesn't put you through the trauma of airport security and budget airlines. Wales.

AT WORK

Since you're reading this book, you may be ahead of the game and I'd be delighted if you would share this information with your workmates and bosses at your place of employment (if you have one). As I've noted above, there are some action lists and resources you can download for free from my website www.strategicalignmentltd.com.

- Talk about it, become a climate bore.

- Tell people about your own plans.

- Tell them where they can find out more information.

- Encourage people to get involved.

- Ask your bosses to set up an employee support programme and participation scheme.

- And make sure they have their own climate strategy.

NATURE

We have to create a collective mindset that natural spaces do not not just offer opportunities to build on but are essential to our well-being. Probably 75% of land and ocean area ought to be left natural, which is about the opposite of what's happening. So far as the UK is concerned, I doubt if even 5% of the land area could be described as truly natural and most of that is in Scotland and Wales. Only 13% of the land area is forested. We've lost a staggering 97% of wild grasslands since 1945. We ought to use the crappiest land on which to build our towns and cities and housing estates and factories and airports and wind and solar farms. Meanwhile (and, globally, I don't foresee the pace of deforestation and habitat loss reversing any time soon, unfortunately), there are a lot of things we can all do to 're-naturalise' – rewilding, it's called – the land spaces we currently occupy. In particular, we need a lot more trees.

- Formal gardens can look lovely but they tend to be rather sterile from the point of view of the bees, butterflies and birds which should be buzzing around them if all were well. Reserve a portion of your garden to let grow wild as a kind of 'cultivated wilderness'.

- Plant meadow grass, wild flowers and trees wherever you can find space.

- Grow your own herbs, fruit and vegetables, and encourage your family and friends to share the delight in doing so.

- Encourage people to grow things in otherwise wasted spaces and to sometimes just let it run wild. I'm thinking of roadside verges, hedgerows, carparks, graveyards, office premises, schools, colleges, churches, hospitals. Talk to your local council about this.

- Reconnect with nature, go for walks, take hiking holidays, do things outdoors and encourage your kids to enjoy life in the wild.

- I know I'm swimming against the tide on this one, but just consider that there are 11 million cats and 9 million dogs in the UK. This – and their support – is a massive industry in its own right. And it's far from 'natural'. Cats kill our wild birds and small mammals. It's what they're good at. Dogs too keep small mammals like hedgehogs at bay. The explosion in pet ownership coincides precisely with the crash in the number of birds and mammals around us.

- Exotic pets such as tropical fish, birds, insects and reptiles are mostly captured from the wild and transported as freight in horrible conditions rather like the battery hens that we're learning to despise. This is a global trade that just should not be happening.

EDUCATION AND EMPLOYMENT

- Educate yourself and your kids about the climate and the environment and check that your local schools do too. Ignorance, wilful and otherwise, is worryingly widespread.

- Under the various climate scenarios, the trend away from conventional employment, jobs and careers, is going to shift even further in ways that are hard to predict. It's possible that kids may reject school and college as a waste of time when faced with a potentially catastrophic future. I do not believe that to be the case. The ability to learn, to adapt, and to figure out new ways of doing things will always be the most valuable survival mechanism.

PEOPLE

- Engage with people and discuss all this. Share your knowledge, insights and concerns. Face up to nay-sayers, and watch out for fake news. The machinations of vested interests are already at play and sometimes it will be hard to figure out what is true and what is not.

- Ignore the rhetoric. Some people will get very opinionated and polarised.

- Americans are amongst the most wasteful people on earth. Reach out to them. Anything they can do will have a proportionately greater impact in helping them save themselves.

- Similarly with people in the developing countries we've mentioned already. If you have any connections there, please use them.

- Write to your government representatives, local and national, and insist they take this seriously. They have a legal obligation to listen to you.

PERSONAL RESPONSIBILITY

We've been fooled for too long by consumer marketing, to the extent that we often don't know that we're being persuaded into buying something that we didn't intend to. The big guns of the consumer world, including pharmaceutical manufacturers, food processors and 'big finance' (amongst others), have so patterned our ways of thinking that we don't even realise we don't need their products. Even if you argue that you do need some of them sometimes, unfortunately the planet doesn't, and it's showing its disapproval through the climate.

- Try to stay objective and fight back against the mental manipulations of marketers persuading us to buy things we don't need.

- Stay healthy and keep away from doctors. Pharmaceuticals are consumed in vast and often unnecessary quantities. Doctors prescribe them by default. Check my book 'Reboot Your Body' for detailed information on nutritional and health tips that can help everyone avoid disease and debility.

- Don't wait for politicians to act – there are no votes in this and the pay off is too far away. Hopefully, this can be made to change with enough of a groundswell.

- The biggest long term threat is the vast population and its growth. Take responsibility by having fewer children and encouraging yours to do the same.

This is a long list of things we all need to do, which reflects the equally long list of things we've been doing wrong. There's no top priority for action. Everything needs attention and it needs it now. That's why we say that saving the planet – saving ourselves – demands a complete change in the way we live our lives. Multiply small things by tens of millions and then change happens.

Coping with your feelings

Many of those who study climate change have reported feelings of depression and overwhelm at the scale of the beast we've unleashed. It's as if everything they've done in their lives is negated by the possibility that it's all in vain. It causes us to question what life is all about, if not preparation for an afterlife nor a constant quest for wealth or the pursuit of possessions.

We each need our own coping mechanism. My own feelings after reading all these reports was a kind of of helplessness against the sheer scale of our unlikely presence in a vast uncaring universe. Dismay that we're not in control after all, that no-one is looking out for us. My response has been to write this book, and to promote a programme of engagement to follow it. People who argue that it's not real and that the science is flawed may be unwittingly responding to the threat emotionally rather than working out their own rational plan. Elisabeth Kübler-Ross long ago set out five stages we tend to go through when faced with loss: denial, anger, bargaining, depression and acceptance. But we're past the denial stage, I'm afraid. There will be plenty of scope for therapists and counsellors in the wake of our present dilemma.

Amongst the scientific community whose voices and evidence I've shared in this book, optimism is in short supply. There was a surge of reports in late 2018 and 2019. But not one of the books, reports and articles I've read offers a solution nor even suggests one is available. Even those who claim to have found a positive gloss struggle to articulate it sensibly. When I first read through the various reports I've reviewed, my immediate response was similarly anxious. But I'm fortunate to possess a rational and analytical mind, so I quickly set out my own assessment of the probability of risk and the likelihood of epic disaster. I concluded that the risk is real and that it is large and that it is virtually impossible to avoid. But there were some 'buts'. The impacts will be wildly different in different parts of the planet. Some places may even have something to gain. Where floods, droughts, tornadoes and hurricanes do strike, it will be – as it has already been – terrible. But there will be other places where weather patterns may shift, where patterns of food production and of disease will change, but where such things can be largely dealt with without too much disruption. As to when it might all take place, well I firmly believe we're in the middle of it. Things will get progressively worse. Some reports and agencies are talking about 2100 as a date with destiny, others 2030. But there is, of course, no single turning point when suddenly everything collapses.

In my view, having assessed the evidence from all sides, it seems that the next ten to twenty years are critical. If we act now, massively, immediately and globally, the worst effects can be held back. But the probability of that great movement of humanity to collectively save ourselves and our planet seems, right now, depressingly low. We have no choice but to take action. If we don't we are sealing our certain doom. If this is the end of the world as we know it, then taking action now is the best medicine, for you personally, for your family and friends, for humanity and for the world.

ABOUT THE AUTHOR

Steve Shelley's environmental credentials include the creation of the UK's 'Bottle Bank' glass recycling scheme, a social change success story of its time. As a professional management consultant, he has carried out strategy assignments for national parks authorities in Kenya, Uganda and Tanzania. He was a co-founder of the Ecotourism Society of Kenya. Steve also has experience of working in the oil industry as a technical advisor.

Steve has travelled extensively in Africa, where he's traversed deserts, rain forests and wide open savannas before humans encroached with their farms, roads and housing schemes. He's seen vast herds of migrating wildlife that give us a clue what the world was like before we came to disrupt it. And he's witnessed the destruction of landscape and loss of habitat that is inflicted in the name of 'progress and development'.

He completed a masters degree in the Leadership of Innovation and Change in 2014.

Steve is based in the UK's Peak District from where he writes books, undertakes consulting assignments, and supports the climate change revolution. He is available to talk to groups to raise awareness of climate change and environmental destruction, spreading the message and helping create more evangelists and advocates.

He's also keen to engage with organisations to advise on climate change, where his expertise in strategy, leadership and change converge with the environment to enable him to help devise pragmatic responses to the pressing challenges set out in this book.

INVITE STEVE TO SPEAK
e-mail climate@steveshelley.org

IF YOU'VE ENJOYED THIS BOOK FROM AMAZON
Please leave a review there!

BY THE SAME AUTHOR

<u>Reboot Your Body</u>: how to stay healthy and live longer

<u>Let's Go Travel</u>: a collection of travel stories to inspire
you to get up and go

A Safari Guide to the Mammals of East and Central
Africa, Macmillan, 1989

A LonePenguin Book
www.thelonepenguin.com

Strategic Alignment Ltd, York, England

LINKS AND REFERENCES

FAO: www.fao.org

IPBES: www.ipbes.net

IPCC: www.ipcc.ch

IPPR: www.ippr.org

NASA: https://climate.nasa.gov/

NOAA: https://www.noaa.gov/

UN Environment: www.unenvironment.org

WWF: www.wwf.org.uk

http://www.scientistswarning.org/

UK Met Office: https://www.metoffice.gov.uk/research/climate/understanding-climate

Greta Thunberg's speech on YouTube:

https://www.youtube.com/watch?v=rYNM4rsnNFM.

INSPIRED BY THE
PEAK DISTRICT